Through the Kaleidoscope blends poetry and biology in a way that will both inspire and educate. It's a breath of fresh air in the conversation between faith and the sciences — and honors both as it unfolds."

— **Mike McHargue**, co-founder of The Liturgists and host of Ask Science Mike

"Elizabeth has found a way to articulate the things we all think but rarely know how to put into words. Her blending of faith and science to draw parallels between what's going on in each of us at both a physical and metaphysical level is spellbinding. Each chapter will give you greater courage to face your deepest questions with confidence that life can and will emerge on the other side!"

— **Ryan May**, Lead Pastor of The Net Church in Chattanooga, TN and author of *Stuck in the Middle*

"Science and faith have often been at odds with one another. Elizabeth Jeffries, though, brings the two together beautifully in *Through the Kaleidoscope*. Her writing is inviting, weaving her love for cell biology with her love for God in powerful, poignant, thought-provoking stories. Jeffries' opens us up to seeing the world of science and faith in a new way — in a way that gives us the space to ask 'What if…' "

— **Rev. Donna Frischknecht Jackson**, editor, *Presbyterians Today* magazine

"Who would imagine that cellular biology would reveal truths about our spirituality and community? As she wrestles with her fundamentalist Christian upbringing, Jeffries deftly explores worlds big and small, weaving together stories and science to give us a new lens on faith."

— **Rev. Sue Washburn**, Pastor of Reunion

Presbyterian Church in Mt. Pleasant, PA

"In this book, Elizabeth Jeffries shows us a world that is less certain and rigid, but far more beautiful, full of life, and vibrant. Each page turn is a turn of the kaleidoscope, revealing unseen facets of all that is within and around us."
— **Blake Chastain**, host of
the Exvangelical podcast

Dear Mom,
Thank you for
all of your support &
always valuing my story!
Love,

Through

the

Kaleidoscope

Through
the
Kaleidoscope

How Exploring Cell Biology
Transforms My Relationship with God

Elizabeth Jeffries

EPIPHANY
PUBLISHING

Published in Indianapolis, Indiana by Epiphany Publishing, LLC.

For information about discounts available for bulk purchases, sales promotions, fundraising, and educational needs, contact Epiphany Publishing Sales at sales@epiphanypublishing.us.

Library of Congress Control Number: 2019938469

ISBN 978-1946093066 (paperback)
ISBN 978-1946093080 (eBook)

This book was printed in the United States of America.

Epiphany Publishing
P.O. Box 36814
Indianapolis, IN 46236
www.epiphanypublishing.us
info@epiphanypublishing.us

CONTENTS

ACKNOWLEDGEMENTS

I have deep gratitude toward:

Kyle Parton and the Epiphany Publishing team, for believing in this book and taking a chance on a new author and an unusual approach.

Blake Chastain and the Exvangelical community, for listening to my story, valuing my experience and giving me a safe place to question, hurt, heal and move forward.

Rob Bell and the November 2017 Something to Say creators, for believing in my vision for this book. Thank you for affirming my story and my voice.

Mike McHargue, Bradley Grinnen and the summer 2018 Making Your Mark OGs, for giving me the tools to grow my story into a book and a platform.

Hot Metal Bridge Faith Community, for being my spiritual home. This community gives me the courage to dig to the foundation of my spirituality and discard the shame while treasuring the deep truths.

My generous and imaginative friends, for reading and critiquing my early draft. Your thoughtful contributions shaped and refined this book in ways I could not have imagined on my own. I'm forever grateful to Lisa Mickey, Andy Soper, Tammy Lynne Ammon, Paul Hufstetler, Joshua Meyer, Heather Reynolds, Chris G. Briggs, Sr., Alexander Richard, Angela L. Smith, Jeff Eddings, Catherine Clendenning, Megan Benton, Justin King-Hall, Keira

Canan, W. Ben Towne, PhD, Barb Wardius, Nikki Morley, Dylan Rooke, Danielle DiVito and Aubrey DiVito.

Mom and Dad, for loving, respecting and celebrating me throughout every stage of my life. Your patience, steadfastness and transparency kept me safe in childhood and inspire me in adulthood.

Ellen Rufft, for suggesting I write down my childhood memories. You believed in me through my darkest days and you bring endless light to my life.

Mark, for refusing to give up on me.

INTRODUCTION

This was the moment I had trained for. All my evangelism classes, Bible study and apologetics courses had been building up to this. I should have been able to handle this conversation and seamlessly direct our dialogue towards our guilt and God's grace. But something wasn't working.

I didn't even realize he had asked a question until I felt the yawning emptiness in the air as he waited for my answer. It was the silence that caught my attention. Suddenly jolted back to the present moment, I felt dampness on my lower back and cottony dryness in my mouth. I racked my brain, trying to remember what he just asked. All I came up with was a repeated mental error message: I hadn't even paid enough attention to piece together a conjecture of the content of his question. It wasn't just the palpable social awkwardness of that moment that embarrassed me. I was embarrassed because I'd worked hard to prepare for conversations like this. Here I was though, just stammering and sweating now that the rubber hit the road.

I was an evangelical. I was born into an evangelical family, and from early childhood, I was taught that my life should have one goal: to win souls for Jesus Christ. I believed that meant convincing others that Jesus deserved their lifelong commitment, and guiding them to pray a prayer declaring their belief and trust in Jesus. Evangelism, for me and for my fellow churchgoers, always started with a personal conversation. People skills were godly characteristics as far as we were concerned. By the time I was twelve, I felt comfortable asking strangers where they expected to spend eternity after they'd die. As a teenager, I went to an evangelism summer camp. I spent hours in evangelism training classes and I read plenty of books about apologetics. So why, now that I was standing in front of this brand-new acquaintance, a non-believer who presented a terrific evangelism opportunity, was I panicking and frozen in my tracks?

I couldn't resort to doing the thing I did every other time I'd seen him that week: stare from a distance and then, when we were closer, pretend that something far away caught my attention and walk quickly past him. I'd already reacted to his question. I couldn't avoid him any longer. His look of confusion was becoming a look of annoyance as the seconds passed, nothing but increasingly awkward silence in the air between us. I mustered a question of my own, my voice cracking through the slight lisp that comes with a bad case of cottonmouth.

"I'm sorry. What's that?"

He knew I heard him loud and clear the first time, but he obliged. "I said, how are you getting along with your roommate?" I was a college freshman, and this was my first week in my dorm. His question was perfectly reasonable and quite thoughtful. It wasn't his question that made me uncomfortable. It was because of something far deeper that I stood there in front of him, frozen and paralyzed with anxiety.

He posed a very particular type of threat, not to my safety or my well-being, but to my worldview. He wasn't the frat boy I'd been warned about, who might try to get me drunk. He wasn't the chatterbox I'd been told to avoid, who might try to entangle me in the freshman dorm rumor mill. He wasn't the philosophy major my youth group leader had cautioned me about, who would try to get me to think my way out of being a Christian. At the time though, I believed that the type of threat he presented, the kind that could undermine my beliefs, was by far the most dangerous.

This freshman dorm was a brand-new frontier for me, and not only for the common reasons. The summer before my freshman year, I received ample and heartfelt warnings from my caring and concerned fellow churchgoers. I'd been taught since childhood that there are two kinds of people in the world: believers and non-believers. The believers were the ones like us, born-again Bible-believing evangelical Christians who declared ourselves to have a personal relationship with Jesus Christ. Everyone else was a non-believer. By issuing warnings, my fellow believers weren't trying to scare me, or even to shame or belittle the people we described as non-believers. They were trying to prepare me. Their concern was in fact valid, and it was rooted in kindness. There are quite a few ways that a non-drinking, non-partying, abstinence-only born-again girl can go off the rails in a public university, and my choices could have potentially damaging repercussions for myself and the people in my life. As it turned out, though, the warnings I received were of little utility. The challenges I faced and the choices I made in college were not the kind that repentance can undo. By the end of those four years, my worldview was irreversibly altered.

It was within the first few days of my freshman year that I met this dorm-mate, the one standing in front of me as I stammered and sweat. It was him and people like him, I'd been taught, that the Bible itself warned about. I believed he was part of a group of people who were undermining God's plan for humanity. I was shocked when a girl on my hall told me that he was one of *them*, and I was equally shocked by how casually and factually she said it. She used a normal tone of voice, not the solemn whisper I was accustomed to hearing when this type of information was communicated. Despite having been taught some incredibly strong opinions and beliefs about this group of people, I'd never actually met one of them before—someone who was gay.

By his very existence, he challenged the strong opinions and beliefs I'd been taught to hold about the gay community. I grew up in the 1990s and early 2000s on a steady diet of Focus on the Family and Rush Limbaugh, and I'd been taught that that the "Homosexual Agenda" was a threat to American democracy, and that every Christian should lament its dangers. It was just as dangerous, I'd learned, as the "Lie of Feminism" or the "Theory of Evolution."

I was taught one consistent narrative about gender and sexuality: males and females have distinct and complementary roles, and God created things to be that way. For a man to be paired with a man or a woman with a woman would be an outright rejection of God's will, we believed. It would be an abomination. Beyond this, I was taught that "The Homosexuals" had an "Agenda," a plan to dismantle and undermine the traditional nuclear family, which we saw as the bedrock of American society.

What made me so uncomfortable about this particular dorm-mate, though, and the reason I stood stammering and sweating in front of him my first week of college, was that he didn't seem dangerous. In fact, he was a really kind person. He, a junior who was established in the social circle of our dorm, was talking to me, an uptight Jesus-loving freshman girl, and he actually seemed to want to be my friend. Over the course of the year, I found even more evidence that he was a really wonderful person. He took the time to remember things about me and he asked me specific questions when we saw each other on campus. He was a careful and hard-working student. In fact, he took his studies more seriously than I did. He was generous, regularly volunteering his time on campus. He was *supposed* to be an abomination; he was *supposed* to hate God and despise families, but instead, his actual life was a clearer image of godly living than any life I'd ever seen up-close. He gave his time freely, but I only volunteered on campus when it would be visible to my church friends. While he paid attention to others, seeming to look for ways to make people laugh, I spent a lot of my time navel-gazing, pondering the pros and cons of every possible course selection and anxiously trying to turn an A into an A+. He was supposed to be a dangerous and abominable person, and my worldview required this to be the case. Instead, he was a contradictory piece of evidence. An anomaly. His existence didn't fit into the Christian worldview I'd embraced my entire life. Something wasn't right.

Getting to know this dorm-mate was the first of many experiences that disoriented me, challenging the assumptions I'd made while growing up in a Bible-believing evangelical Christian community. There were other experiences, too, that were less specific and personal but that clued me in to just how big the world is; much bigger than my circle of homeschooling evangelical Christian families.

When I was twenty-two, I sat on a bench in Washington Square Park, visiting New York City for the first time. Until then, I'd rarely traveled beyond a 50-mile radius of Pittsburgh, Pennsylvania, and the traveling I had done was only to visit family or to go on church-sponsored mission trips. Now, my husband of six months and I were on a weekend trip to NYC, just the two of us and just for fun.

I used to think my city was big, but sitting on that bench, I started to understand how big a city can be. We set on the edge of a pathway around the fountain in the center of the park, and crowds of people were walking, almost buzzing past us. There were so many more people here than

I'd ever seen in one location, and it wasn't just their numbers but it was their diversity that was striking. The park was crowded as usual that day, and each person we saw was visible for a few seconds, then gone, off to continue their day, never to cross paths with us again. I was mesmerized. There were so many different styles of dress, so many different facial expressions and so many different postures in that crowd. All of this, I reminded myself, was only what I saw on the surface. I had no trouble imagining that these crowds represented more backgrounds, more life experiences, more value systems, more dreams, desires and goals than the ones with which I was familiar.

I watched the steady flow of strangers passing by my bench, and just their visible attributes alone — the traits I could see on the surface — were vastly more varied and diverse than anything I'd ever seen. There were passersby of every age, every style of dress, some in obviously expensive suits and accessories, some in torn dirty jeans. I watched a succession of three people, walking one after another, nearly in step. First came a man in a well-tailored high-fashion suit, his face stern and unaffected. He was followed by a teenage girl with a buzz cut and military boots, bright eyed and hinting a smile. She was followed by a man who didn't seem to be walking exactly, but was floating, whose fitted plaid button-down met immaculate, perfectly fitting jeans, the cuffs of which rested at his ankles, elevated gracefully by well-polished 6-inch heeled leather boots.

If it had only been those three faces, the ones I arbitrarily picked out of the buzzing crowd, they alone would have caught my attention. But it wasn't just those three; there were hundreds of faces I glimpsed over the course of the 10 minutes I spent sitting on that bench. Each face belonged to a person. A person with a whole life: responsibilities, relationships, ideas, dreams, disappointments, values, beliefs and hurts. How could I possibly guess what any one of them had experienced in their lives? During my childhood and adolescence, I was completely certain that my world-view, my beliefs and my ideology were the only truth. Ten minutes on that bench were enough to show me just how ridiculous that idea was.

So many of the pressures, expectations and norms of our cultures are arbitrary. I wasn't taught this. I was only taught that the norms of my culture were godly, biblical and had been deliberately chosen. Those college and park bench experiences were some of my very first steps out of the insulation of my religious culture and into the territory of questioning. I've learned to question and often resist the norms of my culture, not only because many of them are arbitrary but because I can plainly see their oppressive, harmful outcomes. Our societal norms and expectations often label, exclude and degrade non-conformers, pushing to the margins those who, by birth or by choice, do not meet these expectations. The only way to break the cycle of this marginalization and exclusion is to question and resist the expectations and norms in our particular culture. The ones that are not robust enough to encompass our actual lives; the ones that our real-life experiences contradict will fall away, making room for the fullness of our human experience.

Each of us has a particular lens. We each see the world from a certain perspective, determined by our personal collection of influences and experiences. There's nothing to be done about this, and there's nothing wrong with this. It's truly the only way any of us can move through the world: by understanding, analyzing and interpreting it from our personal vantage point. The problem is, however, that my lens is just one lens and my experience is remarkably limited. Not only this, but if I surround myself with others who see through the same lens I do, I'm liable to forget that I have a lens at all. It was only at these disorienting times when my lens was failing to bring my surroundings into focus that I became aware of the lens through which I'd been seeing all along. It was at these times that the particularity and the arbitrary nature of my own lens became obvious to me. I could finally see that I had a perspective. With every changing of my perspective, a few of my prejudices and pre-suppositions were exposed, allowing me the capacity to question them. I found evidence that contradicted the things I'd been taught were universal truths, and questioning became my only viable option.

My longing for these opportunities to switch lenses, or even simply to acknowledge my lens, is the reason I wrote this book. This is a book about cell biology, but it's about the aspects of science that extend beyond precise measurement and logical reasoning. It's an exploration of cell biology as a source of metaphors by which I've come to re-think the truths I once believed to be universal. The biological cells that comprise our bodies form communities and these communities have their own ways of operating. Cells are unthinking and unconscious, and their communities are non-hierarchical, but still, biological behaviors follow identifiable patterns that are highly resilient, adaptable and generative. Cells have codes of conduct. From our perspective as observers, these codes of conduct function a lot like social norms.

Cells are tiny enough that they're not included in my commonsense understanding of the world. I can go through my daily life without really thinking about them. They're right here within me, within all of us, but they're invisible without the help of a microscope. Their patterns of behavior and codes of conduct, however, apply to many of the same experiences, issues and challenges you and I face in our human lives. Cells form relationships, make mistakes, and in order to be healthy, must balance the tensions between individuality and community. Cells must remain receptive to outside messengers while also protecting their precious interiors against foreign invaders.

I was born into a group of people who collectively made

a particular set of assumptions about the world and our place in it. Most of us are born into a group of some kind, and whether that group's assumptions are as specific and prescriptive as mine were, or they're more descriptive and general, communities tend to make prevailing assumptions. Some are broad, like assumptions about styles of government or ideal family structures. Some are specific, such as those about the ultimate truth or falsehood of religious axioms. Some are descriptive and some are prescriptive. I adopted more thought patterns and codes of conduct from my community than I realized and today, I'm still discovering more of my own assumptions.

Biological communities of cells parallel our human communities, making it feasible to derive metaphors for the human experience from their behaviors. Cell communities are populated by discrete individuals which together comprise a unified whole. The individuals are mortal and have limited capacities. They interact with one another, sometimes conflicting with their neighbors, and sometimes supporting each other in reciprocity. They form communities and each member plays a specific and essential role. They all rely on each other, no individual able to survive without this communal support.

Beyond simply *forming* communities, cells *are* communities. Each individual is its own community, a collection of diverse specialized pieces. Cells contain powerful engines that transform molecules into energy, sophisticated systems of combat and defense that protect the cell by warding off attackers, elaborate waste disposal systems, and industrious workers cooperating in efficient and robust choreography in order to accomplish it all. The behaviors of these biological communities can serve as metaphors, allowing me to re-think the assumptions I make about my own behaviors.

Cell behaviors inspire me to ask: "what if?" This question's varied forms are the heart of this book, inspiring the possible answers that will be explored in the pages that follow.

"What if it's not correctness and perfect behavior that are expected of me, but instead it's the creativity to work around my weaknesses that will give me strength and wisdom?"

"What if it's not my contribution, but my participation that is of highest value to my community?"

"What if I'm not actually independent from my community, but my neighbors and I have a shared identity, merging over time in deep, fundamental ways?"

To be clear, there's no reason to automatically seek to emulate cell behaviors. I find, though, that asking "what if" allows me to try to see through a new lens. Something beautiful happens when I start to see from a new perspective. All of a sudden, I realize the reality that I saw through my old lens—the one I had all along but never knew was there—was not the one and only truth, but it was simply one image at the end of a kaleidoscope. It was one of many possible images. I can turn that kaleidoscope and watch the image at the end of the chamber transform into an entirely new reality. The more I learn to turn the kaleidoscope, seeing from new perspectives, the more diverse and numerous are the expressions of beauty I can see.

Corrective lenses are useful. They allow me to navigate my finite, immediate surroundings. They bring my concrete, tangible surroundings into focus, sharpening my vision to see precise realities. But not all realities are concrete, tangible and precise. Relationships, community, love, identity, self-perception—all of these are intangible and cannot be measured or quantified. But they are real. These realities shape my life, color my experiences and create my beliefs. Corrective lenses, while lending precision and certainty, are simply the wrong tools for seeing these intangible realities; I need a vision that is expansive and compounding. I need a vision robust enough to accommodate the diversity of ways in which intangible realities can be interpreted. A kaleidoscope reveals infinite, compounding realities, which build on one another as the chamber turns to transform the reflected image. The collective whole of these images is breathtaking and marvelous. I can't help but stare as I turn a kaleidoscope, mesmerized by the continuously shifting, morphing, and transfiguring of the images.

The image at the end of a kaleidoscope chamber appears perfectly symmetrical and highly ordered. There's a striking level of organization in every image. But in reality, the chamber holds a messy pile of colored confetti. Those pieces of confetti — the reality behind all of the mesmerizing images I watch transforming in and out of each other as I turn that kaleidoscope — tumble against each other inside the chamber, falling and flopping as the tube turns, messy, chaotic and in complete disarray. The symmetry is an illusion. It's simply the point of view — the complex system of precisely angled mirrors reflecting the image back to my eyes that masks this messy reality and makes me believe that it's actually orderly and precisely structured.

The beauty of a kaleidoscope can't really be encompassed by rational reduction. A rational analysis — the kind of analysis I conduct as a scientist — would lead me to conclude that what's visible at the end of the kaleidoscope is simply a pile of junk. It's a mess of confetti tossing chaotically around in the end of a tube. But there's more to it than that. What if some realities are not precisely definable? It's only when I consider this possibility that I open myself up to the beauty of the kaleidoscope. I allow myself to take in the transformation of the images, seeing from a new perspective.

My task, then, is to turn the kaleidoscope, and to keep turning it; continuing to seek a new perspective and search for what is common among all of those perspectives. My inspiration is cell biology, a community parallel to my own, complete with its own patterns of behavior, norms and codes of conduct. As I turn the kaleidoscope, I realize that my new understanding of reality is profoundly more robust than it would have been if I insisted on the correctness of the single image I used to see: the one I fought to retain, the one that formed the foundation upon which I built my beliefs and my assumptions. The more images I see, the more fully my vision begins to encompass reality.

To turn the kaleidoscope is to celebrate diverse, multifaceted ways of perceiving reality. It is to celebrate the multiplicity of lenses at my disposal. Turning the kaleidoscope requires trying on new perspectives and asking "what if?" until the answers start to describe reality a little more fully. In order to change lenses, I first need to recognize the particularities of my perspective. This requires excavation. It starts with tracing the genealogies of my ideas, beliefs, assumptions and convictions back to my beginning. We all begin differently, but if we look closely enough, we can each trace our beliefs to a beginning of some sort. For me, I began as a deeply loved, carefully taught and thoroughly indoctrinated child.

1

RENEWING MY MIND

I was the only one causing a problem. Even though everyone else had watched *E.T.* along with me, it was only me who was awake now, crying in the middle of the night. It's not that anyone told me I was causing a problem; they didn't need to tell me. To me, it seemed obvious.

Night after night, my parents came in to calm me down, coaching me to breathe more slowly and more deeply. They spoke reassuring words in calm tones, inviting me to just relax. They told me not to be scared, but that didn't help. Fear wasn't the problem. I was crying because of something bigger. It was something that I certainly couldn't name or describe at seven years old, but it gnawed at me just the same.

This was the third night in a row that I interrupted my parents' sleep with midnight sobbing. They knew it was no mere coincidence that, also three nights ago, we'd watched the film *E.T* as a family.

During the movie I was mesmerized. I sat in the corner of our basement couch, next to my brothers and sister and I couldn't look away from the screen. E.T., the friendly extra-terrestrial creature was displayed on our television screen courtesy of our VCR in 1990s-era grainy low definition. He was so strange, so different from anything I'd ever seen. He was slimy and reptilian but still looked kind of human. He could communicate with Elliot, his human friend, but not the same way that humans communicate. His mannerisms were different, his habits were different, his definition of normal behavior was different. I was drawn to him. Of course, at seven years old, I had no idea why he was so magnetic. All I knew was I'd never seen anything like him, and I couldn't look away.

By night three, the calming routine was well choreographed. The only modification from night to night was the particular parental figure who arrived in my room to calm me down. My dad and mom alternated this duty, and they were both unbelievably quick to come to my rescue—I could barely hear the door *swoosh* open before my dad flipped on the light switch, flooding the room with blinding light. An exasperated "Da-ad" came from my older sister on the trundle bed, inches above the floor beside me. I wasn't just disrupting my dad's sleep; I was disrupting hers, too. I felt suddenly safe as soon as the lights came on. Confusion and disorientation aren't so overwhelming when the lights are shining.

My parents assumed, like any parents would, that I was scared of what I saw in that movie. But really, I was confused. I was confused because everyone else could just watch it, laugh about how silly it was, and then move on. I took it seriously. The movie was about an extraterrestrial creature coming to Earth, which everyone else *knew* was too absurd to be real. The absurdity just wasn't so obvious to me.

There were plenty of other things I could think of, things I'd been told were true, and that everyone else clearly agreed were true, that were so much more absurd than aliens. For instance, I'd been told that stars are really just faraway suns. That seemed completely ridiculous. And that God created the universe out of nothing, an even more outlandish proposition. And that the steady pulsing in my chest was my heart sending blood all around my body. And that I could and should be friends with Jesus Christ. I'd been told that all of these were true, and I trusted the people who'd taught me these things. But now, the very same people who believed all of those absurd truths were drawing the line at aliens.

I've lived twenty-three more years since I first watched *E.T.*, so I've had time to process what I was feeling those nights. I knew back then that there was something magnetic about E.T., something alluring about the idea of an alien. Looking at my grainy television screen, at the image of that slimy reptilian humanoid, I could tell that he was different: he was from some other place. I couldn't articulate it then, but when I imagine extraterrestrials today, I know what it is that makes me excited about the idea of their existence. E.T. promises to provide something I ache for: a new perspective.

A few years before watching *E.T.*, I asked my mom about the stars we saw in the sky at night. I wanted to know what they were. She told me that those tiny pinpricks of light are very far-away suns. Of course, I thought, those suns must have planets like ours, and those planets would have people or creatures like us. Well, like us but different. The thought of extraterrestrials was exciting. I wanted something else to exist beyond my familiar surroundings. I wanted there to be more.

The spaceships have not yet arrived, but I have found what I hoped the extraterrestrials would provide. As a human, I am a conscious being but I'm also a biological creature. I'm made of cells, and from the point of view of any one of my cells, my body is like a universe. My cells are composed of organelles, proteins and DNA, and to any one of these components, a single cell is like a world of its own. My biological self is a foreign parallel world, separate from my human experience but contained within it all along.

I spent a decade in higher education studying the natural sciences, and I learned rational explanations for cell behaviors. Predictability and order, I was taught, are essential characteristics of science. And it's true; I never have to look far to find evidence of the power and utility of the scientific method. Scientific explanations, order and predictability are real, important and powerful. Hospitals, bridges, cars and airplanes would not exist without the practical explanatory power of science. But the explanations, the order and the predictability do not fully encompass biological behavior. Cell biology also tells stories. There's more to it than facts. The stories that can be seen in the inner workings of cells are stories about relationships, purpose, community and identity. They're parables, and many of them teach unorthodox lessons. They show me how idleness can actually be more productive than activity. They show me that some flaws are best left unrepaired. The morals of these biological parables are surprising, and they give me new ways of thinking about my own life. They give me alternatives to ideas and explanations that have grown too familiar.

The reason I'm drawn to these biological parables is

because that feeling still returns — the feeling I had when I was seven, crying at midnight. I was experiencing what all kids experience: I was being taught that the world works in one particular way, and I was surrounded by people who were very sure that this was the case. I felt that I was the only one who saw things differently, and I felt alone in my confusion. Even with my limited seven-year-old capacity, it was a moment of emptiness and loneliness, and it was the first of many.

Throughout my childhood and young adulthood, my parents and my church community worked hard to give me a stable, secure world. This was a privilege that has benefitted me in ways I'm continually discovering. But humans make assumptions, and my human community tended to reinforce those assumptions rather than challenge them. We accepted overly simple answers to complicated questions. We hastily distilled complex, multifaceted concepts into pairs of mutually exclusive opposites and we assumed that to reject one was to embrace its opposite. We established many of our norms through presumption and tradition. Even though I couldn't articulate it at the time, there was something about the very thought of E.T. that drew me in when I was seven years old. It renewed my mind to imagine extraterrestrials. It was a reprieve from all the assumptions, conventions and mutually agreed-upon ways of thinking, behaving and relating that I saw around me. Now as an adult, the patterns of behavior I see in cell biology provide that same reprieve.

The most important social convention in my community had to do with Jesus Christ. When I was three years old, far too young to understand what I was doing, I gave my heart to Jesus and became born-again. I was at home in the living room, leaning against the edge of the couch with my bare feet on the avocado green shag carpet. I loved that carpet. It made a perfect make-believe lawn outside of my Lego Barbie mansion, and it felt pillowy, the soft threads long enough that I could bury all my toes.

My big brother, ten at the time, asked me if I'd asked Jesus into my heart. I knew who Jesus was and what my heart was but I had no idea how Jesus would get inside of it. I knew my heart pumped my blood, the blood I could feel pulsing through my wrists. That pulse got even stronger and faster now that we were talking about heaven and hell.

I heard about Jesus more than I heard about anything else. I saw his face every morning in my picture Bible. Our whole family would sit in the living room every morning to have devotions. We read from the Bible, sang a worship song and prayed for every item on our prayer request list. Jesus was there in my picture Bible: the guy with a bloody, agonized face, crushed under the weight of the cross he carried on his back. Jesus was the one who I killed with my sins. I knew I was supposed to feel sorry for him, but I didn't even know him. We'd never met him but everyone in my family was very sure that they loved him. Of course, I quickly told my brother that I wanted to ask Jesus into my heart. It was the least I could do after having killed him with my sin.

I repeated the words my brother said, the words that were supposed to change everything. My eternal destiny was determined now; I had a mansion in heaven and I'd be spared from hell. But over time, through my childhood and adolescent years, having Jesus in my heart clarified very little, and in fact it introduced a lot of brand-new questions. If God loves me, why had God been planning to send me to hell forever? If I deserve to go to hell, how does Jesus get away with going behind God's back to get me into heaven?

Isn't that cheating? If God has a good plan for our lives, why do people who love God still get sick? If God created me to need food in order to live, why is gluttony a sin? And how can I tell if I'm a glutton? Questions emerged in my mind, but I was told it was a sin to question God. If my faith was strong enough, they said, my questions would go away. Then to top it all off, I was told the most absurd thing of all, the opposite of what my experience told me was true: that Jesus Christ was the key to making sense of my existence.

We all learn specific ways to think and behave. Relationships, work, personal identity, community responsibility, self-discipline; we each are given codes of conduct for navigating our lives. Usually these codes of conduct are absorbed from our communities, whether we're given explicit instructions or if we're left to decipher appropriate behavior for ourselves. For me, codes of conduct were explicitly taught and were rooted in a particular form of American evangelical Christianity. I learned patterns of thinking and behaving, and I didn't naturally recognize that these were specific to my culture, my place in history and my family. They were not universal. It was only when I found myself seeing things differently from other people in my community that I began to realize that my culture was specific and arbitrary.

My community taught me my vocabulary, my ways of thinking, and my ways of behaving. During the years between my midnight sob sessions and now, I've been continuously marinating in my earthly culture. Unless I question it, unless I work to gain new perspectives, it becomes more and more difficult to notice the specificity of my culture. What surrounds me becomes my default mode of operation, and eventually, it's second nature. To override it is difficult, and requires a conscious choice. But you and I have the freedom to make this choice.

The exercise of this freedom requires imagination. It requires a renewal of the mind. This is what I tearfully wished the aliens would give me, and it's what I've found in the biological world of cells. I see a parallel, foreign world that sparks my imagination and gives me a chance at transcending my culture.

The biological world is independent of the forces that shape my human culture. Cells don't have awareness and consciousness the way we do. Cells are uninfluenced by politics, religion, economics and social norms. Gene expression, DNA replication and mitosis are independent of emotions and social mores. But cells do have particular ways of behaving. These ways of behaving are not automatically better or worse than mine, they're just different. These stories perform the most powerful service a story can provide: they spark my imagination. I don't have to imagine extraterrestrials in order to renew my mind; I can look to the communities of cells existing within my own body.

For me, biological parables are more than just interesting; they spark my imagination and give me the ability to re-think the assumptions and norms that I've adopted. They allow me to re-see the world as if for the first time. They allow me to renew my mind, and this renewal is the first step toward transformation.

Renewing my mind makes the entire world suddenly new. I find that this renewal shows me that the terrain is quite a bit bigger, more complex and more colorful than the map that I inherited had led me to believe.

2

SOWING AND REAPING

Dinnertime every night was an event of its own. It was more than a meal for us; it was a family meeting, and I mentally prepared for it all day long. We'd go around the table, starting with my mom and ending with my dad, each of us sharing a story about something that happened that day.

My dad took his turn last, having listened to everyone else's stories before his, asking us thoughtful questions about our daily experiences. He always made me feel that my day's activities were important and that what I had to say was meaningful. Even though I was a just a kid, and the youngest in the family by several years, my parents made me feel that I had something valuable to add.

My dad told his stories differently from the rest of us. His stories were chosen carefully. For him, conversations were opportunities for teaching and encouraging others, and he intentionally and caringly magnified this capacity when he spoke to his young children. His daily anecdote was usually interwoven with a lesson of some sort.

"That's what happens when you make poor choices." His eyes were wide and concerned, his head slowly shaking back and forth. His voice was sad and serious, with a cautionary tone. He was warning us about a very real and threatening danger. Growing up with an attorney father who ran a small private practice, I became familiar with life's common legal pitfalls. Bankruptcy was high on that list.

The stories were always similar: tens of thousands of dollars in credit card debt, car loans, student loans, and an unreasonably high mortgage. Not enough income to cover the charges, bills and debts, and eventually the expenses caught up with them. Selfishness and frivolity finally got the best of them, and they now found themselves at my dad's law office to file for bankruptcy.

"It couldn't be simpler," my dad said from his seat at the head of the dinner table. He was fully in his teaching mode now. "You reap what you sow. If you plant seeds of selfishness, you'll reap your own downfall."

"You reap what you sow" was our way of saying that people get what they deserve. This was how we explained the inequities we saw in our world. We told ourselves that wealthy people must have managed their finances well enough to deserve their mansions, and that those living outside on the city streets in the cold must have squandered their money — or their ability to earn money — and now were reaping destitution. From this perspective, every success or struggle had a cause.

The "reap-what-you-sow" principle has an obvious concrete meaning. It's based in nature: if lettuce seeds are planted in a garden, it would be foolish to expect zucchini plants to grow. Cherries will never be harvested from an apple tree. In the biological realm, actions have reactions and causes bring about effects.

For us, though, as Bible-believing Christians, this principle was more than just a plant-based metaphor. It was part of the holy scriptures. It appears throughout the Bible, and the pattern of sowing and reaping is presented as a basic reality, not only in nature but in human experience as well. The pattern is reinforced in Galatians 6:7-8, where Paul introduces the idea of sowing and reaping, extending a simple agricultural concept to encompass the cause-and-effect relationships we experience in our daily lives. It seems that personal responsibility, in Paul's view, reigns supreme in the Kingdom of God. Whether someone is in trouble or they're prospering happily, the comprehensive "reap-what-you-sow" principle suggests they did something along the way to deserve it.

I imagined my life to be a blank canvas, only to be filled with the image that my actions, attitudes and prayers would create. American individualism amplified the notion of agency and independence prevalent in my family's form of evangelical Christianity. In a doctrinal stance formed largely in reaction against the Calvinistic notion of predestination, we believed we had influence over our lives, that we had power to create our own futures and agency to make our own choices. We coupled this concept with a belief in the power of prayer: we believed in a God who would respond to our prayers by intervening, disrupting the current course of things in order to bring us the protection, peace, financial assistance, or healing we requested. We believed we had power to influence our own lives, either through the purity of our behaviors or the fervor of our prayers. This religious concept of agency can be empowering, but when paired with our emphatic belief in total human depravity, it created a ground fertile for the growth of anxiety and guilt.

Simple formulas like "reap-what-you-sow" are bound to break down at some point. For me, the very first time I remember it breaking down was a literal breakdown. It was a summer weekday afternoon and I was at the magical age when my phonics skills had finally brought me into the realm of independent reading. The whole world seemed exciting. Something about that newfound ability kicked my curiosity into high gear, delighted by the increasing ease with which I could decode previously inscrutable street signs and gas station letter boards.

We were all in the car, the whole family except my dad, and we were about a mile from home when our maroon 1985 Colt Vista came to a sputtering halt. My mom steered us out of traffic and drifted the vehicle safely onto the curb. We walked carefully in single file to the nearest gas station and used the pay phone. She made a call to my dad at his office, who sent a tow truck right away. The tone of their voices let me know that we were in trouble, and it was bigger trouble than just needing a ride home.

The tow truck driver dropped us off at home, then took the vehicle to the shop. I was too young to understand or follow all of the details, but later that night, the mechanic called with the bad news that no one in our house had mentioned as a possibility but everyone quietly anticipated. The Vista had broken down once and for all. The cost of repairs would exceed the worth of the vehicle. As an elementary school-aged child, all that I knew at the time was that our family's only mode of transportation was gone.

The next morning, our family devotional time was quieter than usual. We always approached our devotional times with earnestness, but today we were especially serious and somber. We went through each step of our devotions, just as we typically did. We read the Old Testament chapters that were on our plan for the day in our Bible-in-a-year plan, then we moved on and read our New Testament chapters. We sang our worship song, and then we got ready for prayer time. We kept a prayer list and updated it every day with details of every prayer request that any of us had. No request was too insignificant or too grand for this list. I prayed for healing for family members suffering from chronic illnesses and I prayed that I'd have fun at my Brownie girl scout troop meetings. We believed in a God who was equally interested in every aspect of our human experience. On this day, we added a new line to our prayer request list: "Buy a new car." This line remained unanswered on our prayer list for nine months.

I was, for the very first time, asking a truly perennial question that had been asked by so many others across the globe and over centuries of history, many in incredibly painful, serious and devastating circumstances. I was still a child and I wasn't in true danger or distress, but even so, I felt this question echoing inside of me, never answered but only giving rise to more and more questions. This was the first time I asked God "*why?*" Why would God let us down after we'd done our part? I knew my family was careful — meticulous, even — with money, and we were praying diligently, but nonetheless, our prayers remained unanswered.

This was the first of many seasons of questioning for me. Having been raised to believe that everyone reaps what they sow, I felt as though my life was a continuous series of tests. As I got older, I believed that the grades I received, the friends I made, my seat placement in the cello section of the orchestra — really everything that occurred in my life was a "harvest" that I reaped as a direct outgrowth of the seeds I'd sown. Even in times when these "harvests" were benefits that I enjoyed, I still felt a strain. My belief in my own agency left me toggling between anxiety and guilt. My guilt was the ugly outgrowth of my belief that my struggles were my own fault; that I created them either through my poor choices or my lack of prayer. My anxiety was the self-directed pressure stemming from my belief that when things were going my way, it was because of my prudent choices. Therefore, I cannot afford to stumble. My belief that I had agency to create my own future only empowered me in the fleeting present moment. When I examined my past or planned for my future through the lens of this belief, I became trapped in a cycle of anxiety and guilt. The alternative to this cycle, though, never seemed any better. To believe that my actions were irrelevant, I imagined, would only result in hopeless depression. None of my options seemed great.

As a young adult caught up in this struggle, believing in my own agency and yet experiencing an unfair world, it's no wonder I gravitated toward the natural sciences. Science seemed to render the world predictable, logical and concrete. The scientific method provides a way of systematically dissecting reality. Before we even begin this dissection, we assume that events have causes. Actions have reactions. Outcomes follow predictably from events.

There was something about the microscopic realm of nature that especially attracted me. It seemed so fundamental, the realm of the basic realities that undergird the complex tapestries of macroscopic life. The microscopic world is hidden from the everyday observer, our natural perspective far too obtuse to recognize this ever-present complexity. Yet, it's present in every aspect of our existence. By the time I was in graduate school, I was working in molecular biology, the world of microscopic biological systems. Although cells are microscopic entities, they are themselves universes. Contained within each cell is an elaborate system of interacting and interrelating parts and pieces. We can zoom in even further, passing the cell and bringing into focus the molecules that compose these living cells: DNA, RNA and proteins.

When I started to become serious about studying science in high school and college, my textbooks were filled with examples of predictable cause-effect relationships, and these examples seemed to be airtight. Nature seemed to be reducible. Flowcharts filled the margins of my books, depicting mechanisms of enzyme action. My professors described step-by-step domino effects of molecular actions.

The scientific journal articles that I would read usually concluded with a paragraph detailing a proposed mechanism of action. It was a description of the observed effect in terms of stepwise actions, reactions and interactions. It seemed that all we'd have to do as molecular biologists would be to conduct our research meticulously enough, and we'd be able to disentangle every cause of every outcome. It seemed like I'd found the molecular equivalent of the predictability and fairness I wished I could find in my human world. In the realm of these unthinking, unconscious subcellular molecules, that which was sown was always reaped.

My understanding of molecular biology started to change when I moved beyond the structure of my classrooms and textbooks. Toward the end of college and the beginning of graduate school, I started to read and study scientific journal articles. I started following stories that were not fully curated, reading about biological elements that hadn't been neatly characterized, and tracking down proteins whose functions could not yet be concisely summarized. While my textbooks listed carefully selected examples of processes whose outcomes were well-documented and reactions whose functions were clearly known, reality contained plenty of exceptions: cellular processes and reactions whose outcomes and functions were numerous and diverse. These were cases in which one event could create one of multiple divergent and ostensibly unrelated outcomes. I was beginning to learn about a layer of complexity that I'd never before encountered in natural systems.

A protein named ubiquitin is a perfect example of the diversity and complexity I was beginning to observe. When I first heard the protein's name, assigned because of its ubiquity, I assumed that it must have a universal, non-specific role. Despite its presence in the vast majority of cell types within our bodies though, ubiquitin has no specific solitary function. It's a tiny protein, a fraction of the size of most proteins found inside our cells, and it's prone to attach itself to its much-larger cellular protein neighbors. When it does so, it becomes incredibly powerful, initiating a dramatic cellular response. Oddly though, the possible ultimate outcomes of that cellular response vary wildly.

In a well-documented manner, ubiquitin attaches itself to a target protein and efficiently and systematically destroys this target (Ciechanover 1980; Hershko 1980). The effect is so dramatic and difficult to block or derail that ubiquitin has been nicknamed the molecular "kiss of death." This targeted destruction is one of the ways that overly abundant or dysfunctional proteins are removed from our cells, a service essential to the health of our cells.

This is, however, by no means the only, or even the main function of ubiquitin. Molecular biologists have observed that ubiquitin-tagging can bring about cellular events that are wildly distinct from waste removal, and the list of possible outcomes is continually growing longer and more diverse. Ubiquitin not only attaches itself to proteins, but it can also attach itself to DNA molecules. DNA is the biological master molecule, forming the basis of cell functions. It provides the recipe for every protein that each cell produces. Our cells "read" our DNA molecules, and through **transcription** and **translation**, generate proteins based on the genetic sequence in the DNA molecules. The proteins that a cell produces form the traits of that cell, the traits of cells make up the traits of organs, and the traits of organs make up the traits of a person. A glitch—damage, in the form of a break or a mutation—in a single DNA molecule has profound reverberations, deeply and often detrimentally impacting the traits of the person. Each DNA molecule must engage in the correct chemical reactions at the correct time, location, rate and for the correct duration in order to keep a person alive and healthy. Maintaining healthy DNA strands and fixing broken DNA strands are clearly essential functions for keeping cells—and the people those cells compose—healthy.

Ubiquitin provides a specialized service within our cells, having the unique ability to repair otherwise irreparable DNA breaks. Ubiquitin can detect sites of damage in DNA strands. The tiny protein does so by binding to histones, the proteins that function as spools, around which the DNA strands are wound into tight coils inside of cells. Ubiquitin, by binding and "physically disrupting" these spools, "allows access for DNA repair proteins" to fix breaks buried so deeply in the spool that they could be repaired in no other way (Dwane 2017).

This isn't the only means by which histone-bound ubiquitin can facilitate the repair of broken DNA. The tiny protein's attachment can also occur as part of a chain of communication within the cell, binding in response to detection of a damaged region in the DNA molecule (Schwertman 2016). Their histone attachment sends a series of molecular signals cascading throughout the cell, resulting in the deployment of the cellular DNA repair tools.

There are still other ways in which ubiquitin affects histone proteins. For instance, ubiquitin can bind to a histone protein and modulate the expression of a nearby gene, altering the abundance of the protein produced by that gene. Even when ubiquitin's target is the exact same protein — histone proteins — the outcome of its attachment can vary broadly.

This protein is a wild card. How can one molecular event yield such dramatically different results? A single molecule can trigger waste removal, modulation of gene expression, repair of DNA damage via multiple pathways, or any one of an ever-growing list of further cellular outcomes.

It's not ubiquitination, the molecular event itself, that determines the cellular outcome. The molecular event is simply the introduction of a new fork in the road. The inner workings of cells are mind-bogglingly complex. Cells are not monolithic machines. They are communities. We're made out of billions of molecular communities that are each made up of proteins, DNA, RNA and organelles which interact, intertwine and mutually influence one another. These communities are diverse: long, wispy nucleic acid strands wind tightly around blobby proteins only to unwind again upon receiving a signal that it's time for the cell to proliferate. Tiny proteins latch firmly onto massive proteins, just to release again when they're needed more urgently elsewhere. Key-shaped active regions fit perfectly into lock-shaped receptors, attaching and detaching in precise choreography. Each individual participates in a unified whole, coordinating and communicating to create our traits.

Myriad contextual factors determine which of the divergent paths the cell takes once it encounters that fork in the road, the one presented by ubiquitin. What is the specific identity of the target? That will affect its fate. What other molecules are nearby? That will affect its fate. Is the target actively accomplishing something at the time of ubiquitination? That will affect its fate. None of these factors unilaterally determines the result, but each one contributes to the result. The cell contains a community, and inside of it is an ocean teeming with proteins in search of interacting partners, enzymes in search of DNA molecules, ligands in search of substrates. Tiny ubiquitin, so small it could be mistaken for a fragment of any one of the other proteins it's bumping up against, is tossed in the waves of this molecular ocean. Every force that ubiquitin encounters in the cell plays a role, each factor contributing in some way to the cellular community. This community is the context that collectively determines the fate of the ubiquitinated molecule.

When we investigate our biological interiors, we don't see linear domino effects. Instead, we see splintering paths, many of which have escape routes and opportunities for reversal. The more we learn about the molecular workings of our cells, the more numerous and diverse these splintering paths become. New opportunities are in constant supply: opportunities for action, reaction, reversal, modification, cooperation, or engagement in parallel pathways. The details of a cell's interior have the power to transform the molecular events within that cell.

My human experience has a lot in common with cells' interiors. I'm not isolated, and I'm not independent. I am the product of my family, socioeconomic status, professional surroundings and political environment. I'm a product of the ideas, beliefs and priorities that prevail in my community. Ultimately, I'm the product of my experience, shaped and defined by my communities and contexts. It would be nonsense to predict the result of ubiquitination unless I'm considering its full cellular context. Likewise, it would be nonsense to draw precise lines connecting my individual actions with their effects, unless I'm also considering my own full cultural context.

My American culture places a high value on individuality, and my evangelical Christian community emphasized a doctrine of personal salvation. This cultural context provided me with a strong narrative of personal agency. I was taught that I can lift myself up by my bootstraps. I've been led to believe that both poverty and wealth are self-made, that happy relationships are the result of hard work and sacrifice while troubled ones are the fault of the individuals' selfishness. The interiors of our cells offer a new image. It's an image of the complexity of life and of the formative effects of context.

While it remains true, in a sense, that we reap what we sow, we don't all sow into the same soil. The seeds we each sow, such as our frugality, restraint and honesty, are sown in relation to our surroundings. My actions will yield a different result from another person's actions, because we each start from different places. We begin at distinct positions of power and privilege, different points of opportunity. We try to draw straight lines between the virtue of our actions and the circumstances of our lives, but context obscures any direct or precise correspondence.

While we each exert a measure of agency, the outcomes of the seeds we sow — the harvest we reap — will be determined by factors that are outside of our control.

The molecular events that occur within a cell, such as the attachment of ubiquitin to a target molecule, are only understood within the context of what else is happening inside the cell. There are interactions, processes and mechanisms already in motion, and any new event will certainly be influenced by these. What is most striking about the inner workings of cells is that their contextual factors do not simply influence reality — they transform it.

What if I view my own personal choices in this light? This metaphor of biological complexity allows me to begin making sense of the entanglement of personal agency and context. I was dealt a particular hand, as was every other person. I inherited a certain set of practical opportunities, I was born into a physical body that has particular abilities and attributes, and I adopted perceptions, beliefs and values that shape my understanding of the world. I was born into a system that was already in motion long before I arrived. When I started choosing, acting, planning and deciding, I was already swimming in an ocean made of the outcomes of others' choices.

It can feel defeating to think of myself in this way: adrift in an ocean of factors I cannot control, reaping the fruits of seeds I did not sow. Why try to sow seeds of persistence, compassion and frugality if I'm just going to reap the fruit of someone else's laziness, judgment and frivolity? My efforts seem futile.

But there's more to the story. Human communities are deeply connected, and though the effects of my actions may not always be directly traceable to my choices, those effects are real and powerful. It may seem that I'm swimming in an ocean made by other people's choices, but if I look to my right and my left, I see others who are swimming in this ocean alongside me. I can think of those who have been creating these waves for millennia, and I can imagine ahead to those who will swim in this ocean long after I'm gone. The fruits of the seeds I sow might not be harvested by me, but they will be harvested by someone. Every drop of water in this ocean has an origin.

I can detach myself from the strictly mechanistic view of my actions and their outcomes, and also remain persistent in my efforts to sow the seeds whose fruits I want to reap. My actions, while they don't determine outcomes in a predictable and linear fashion, do determine possibilities. Actions facilitate trends that are already in motion within a community. A ubiquitin molecule alone, attached to a histone protein, will not trigger the action of the cell's DNA repair mechanism. It requires helpers, target proteins that are healthy enough to accept it, and downstream actors to continue transmitting the DNA repair signals until the job is done. However, if ubiquitin never attaches to the histone proteins, DNA repair can never be triggered by this mechanism. The insufficiency of each isolated factor to complete the process doesn't invalidate the indispensability of each one.

As an evangelical Christian kid, I grew up learning Jesus' teachings about unity. I was taught a specific meaning for unity: unity meant that Christians have membership in an exclusive group. I believed we were set apart from the rest of the world, and that there was something distinguishing *us* from *them*. This teaching intensified my human tendency to look for dividing lines; ways to distinguish between groups of people. After studying my own cellular interiors, though, unity takes on a new meaning. The concept of unity now opens my eyes to the complexity of communities: regardless of whether I admit it, know it or even like it, I am unified with my communities. I sow and reap in interdependent, interconnected and thoroughly entangled ways.

I'm composed of molecules that tell complex, easily

obscured and situation-dependent stories. Biology is complicated, interdependent and messy; yet, in the book of Galatians, Paul used a biological parable to teach the value of personal responsibility. Biology is the story of community, the emergence of something greater than the sum of its parts. Cells and the bodies they compose can open our eyes to see how sophisticated realities emerge from the choreography of seemingly discrete individual pieces. The contributions of one individual part are actually much less deterministically impactful than I once thought. But they aren't irrelevant. My actions intertwine, interact and react with their communal contexts, reverberating throughout the entire emerging whole. I am part of something much greater than myself.

3

THE WORD OF GOD

It wasn't a mealtime, and I honestly shouldn't have been eating right then anyway, but all of that is beside the point. The point is that the note was always there. It was a reminder written in cursive handwriting on a 3"x5" ruled index card. The card hung right at eye level on the refrigerator door, impossible to miss. I was never far from this index card reminder. As a homeschooler, I spent the vast majority of my time in this house and passed through the kitchen numerous times per day. The message on the index card was ominous, but I didn't read it as a threat. It was a warning, issued to protect me from an ever-present danger. The index card displayed Philippians 3:18-19:

"For many, of whom I have often told you and now tell you even with tears, walk as enemies of the cross of Christ. Their end is destruction, their god is their belly, and they glory in their shame, with minds set on earthly things."

As a 12-year-old who wholeheartedly wanted never to be classified as an "enemy of the cross of Christ," I was grateful for this verse. I was grateful to be warned before it was too late. So many of the Bible's warnings and instructions had to do with my heart, my mind and my beliefs, those parts of me that were confusing, elusive and hard to pin down. Philippians 3, however, with the specificity of its description of evil — "their god is their belly" — gave me details. It gave me something concrete and tangible. That phrase was the reason the index card was here, on the front of the refrigerator, right at eye level where everyone in the family would see it multiple times each day: "their god is their belly." If the verse had simply warned against "setting our minds on earthly things," it would have been harder to know how to comply. Gluttony, however, was a sin associated with our behavior. Gluttony could be quantified a little more easily.

At 12, I was newly familiar with the quantifiable aspects of my eating habits. Puberty had arrived early for me and my body seemed so different and new now. Existing in a rapidly transforming body, and one that was changing faster than the other girls' my age, had begun to diminish my sense of control. By age 10, I'd reached my adult height of 5'2" and within the next two years, my weight steadily climbed, beginning to reach an unhealthy point.

I was taller, softer and rounder than the other girls my age. This was not entirely new; for as long as I could remember, I'd thought of myself as chubby. My face looked softer than other girls' faces; when I straightened my arms, my elbows turned into little dimples that bulged out on all sides, and my knees looked perfectly round and fleshy when I was sitting in a chair, without any knobby bones poking out like they did on other girls' knees. My weight had bothered me my whole childhood, but until now, it had all just been a matter of aesthetics.

Now, at age 12, my weight was a different type of issue. At my last appointment with my doctor, my blood pressure reading was high. My doctor noted that the extra weight on my body was certainly not *un*related to my high blood pressure, so she suggested I make an effort to lose weight. Weight loss took on a new urgency and importance now, having become more than an aesthetic endeavor. It was now a health priority.

I learned about calories, fat grams, BMI and BMR and discovered that, much to my relief, weight management was simple arithmetic. Equipped with a doctor-recommended low-fat, low-sodium, low-cholesterol diet and a handwritten food journal that I updated after each meal, I had the tools to regain control. It was relieving to have a plan to manage my own weight. I was self-conscious, overweight, and living in a rapidly transforming body; I was desperate to gain some form of control. Now I had the means of quantifying my food intake and my exercise calorie burn, and I was looking forward to making some progress.

My eating habits meant even more to me, though, as a Bible-believing evangelical Christian kid. Food could not be fully reduced to just arithmetic, and it was about more than healthy living or aesthetics. In my mind, this was spiritual work. If I could learn to manage my weight, then I told myself there would be no question: Philippians 3 couldn't possibly be about me.

The index card was always there on the fridge, either a stern reprimand or a congratulatory "'atta girl." The verse was there when I was sneaking an extra piece of cheese that was not approved by my diet plan, quickly and secretively shoving it into my mouth. It was also there each time I walked right past the pantry without digging around inside, despite my rumbling stomach. In these moments, the swelling of my pride made me forget about all the guilt I felt when I succumbed to gluttony. *See? My stomach is not my god.* In my mind, food decisions were spiritual battles and there was nothing sweeter than emerging victoriously.

In these moments of victory, I felt that I'd won. I'd successfully made it out of the kitchen and upstairs, away from the temptations of food. However, the rush of pride would soon diminish because, despite my growing hunger pains, despite my diligence in recording my food intake, and despite my persistence in exercising for 30 minutes daily, I still looked the same. *Maybe I'm still not doing enough, I thought. Maybe I'm still a glutton after all.*

Or maybe it was the angle. The full-length mirror attached to the inside of my bedroom closet door was perfect for my at-least-daily self-scrutiny sessions. I pushed the door open just a bit more, searching for a better angle. Leaning my torso upward and forward, stretching out my spine and arching my back ever so slightly, I studied my midsection. The fat on my tummy became a little less visible the more I exaggerated my lean and the more I sucked in my stomach. It was even better if I contorted my spine and strained my neck a little bit.

No amount of contorting could take away this feeling, though. I didn't know any other girls my age who seemed to have this struggle. My friends seemed so effortlessly thin. They seemed to have natural self-control. They didn't need food diaries. They didn't have high blood pressure. I was the only one who needed the food diaries and the weekly blood pressure readings, and it seemed I was the only one who had a problem with gluttony. I could always hold out hope, though, that gluttony wasn't exactly my problem. *Maybe I just have a bad metabolism*, I thought.

I was eight years old the first time I heard about metabolism, calories and fat storage, and this new information simultaneously relieved and frustrated me. I was relieved because I could see that my damning sin of gluttony was not the only possible explanation for my chubbiness. I was frustrated, though, because it meant that if my metabolism was just worse than others', then I'd have to work harder than everyone else in order to achieve a slender physique.

Still standing in front of my mirror, I exhaled and everything fell back into its regular place. The misplaced curves, the bulges—my chubbiness was fully apparent to me once again.

The cliché was lost on me. I was a twelve-year-old American female standing in front of a full-length mirror inside my bedroom closet, squeezing, twisting, contorting and sucking, trying to decide if I was fat or not. The vanity, the desperation for approval and praise, the preoccupation with the opinions of strangers—all of it was obnoxiously self-consumed. But I was convinced that my weight loss efforts and my self-scrutiny had nothing to do with vanity. To me, this was truly spiritual work. I was convinced that by fighting desires, cravings and comforts, I was putting God first, ahead of my selfish desires.

Just above the upper left-hand corner of the mirror, was a Bible verse on an index card, held to the frame with tape. This one was written in my own handwriting. The verse was found in one of the only Old Testament books that made any sense to me: Proverbs. The verse was Proverbs 31:30:

"Charm is deceitful, and beauty is vain, but a woman who fears the Lord is to be praised."

I'd written this verse out and taped it above my mirror so that I'd remember why I was counting my calories, going for daily aerobic walks in my neighborhood and eating an apple for dessert instead of a cookie. Diminishing the fat layer around my midsection would be an outward sign of my fear of the Lord, I thought. Proverbs 31:30 reminded me to keep focusing on this fear of the Lord, not on vanity as a motivation to lose weight. In my mind, I was proving that I loved and feared God more than I loved food.

These Bible verses from Proverbs and Philippians were not the only ones posted around our house. We had a verse for every part of our lives, and to us, each verse was a precious gem that had been mined from the biblical text. We took the complex, poetic and often absurd biblical texts, with their bizarre comments about appropriate interactions with menstruating women, proper treatment of slaves and the importance of women staying silent in church, and we extracted concrete instructions for our lives, here in America at the turn of the 21st century. Philippians 2:14 was posted in the kitchen next to the list detailing our household chores: "Do all things without grumbling or disputing." Psalm 4:8, printed in my own handwriting, was posted on my nightstand: "In peace I will both lie down and sleep; for you alone, O Lord, make me dwell in safety." And, of course I posted the perennial classic Philippians 4:13 on my homeschool textbook bookshelf: "I can do all things through him who strengthens me."

These Bible verse index cards were neither a gesture nor a performance. I posted them with no one but myself in mind. I wanted to get these words in my own mind, so they would become part of my own internal monologue. I wanted these verses to shape my thoughts and determine my actions. I intentionally hung index card verses in places where I'd see them multiple times each day. Once I became familiar with one verse, I'd rotate it out, moving on to something less familiar. Biblical study and memorization were compounding pursuits; I wanted to progressively, continuously expand my understanding of the Bible and broaden my repertoire of memorized Bible verses.

In my church, we talked about the Bible using military metaphors, saying we wished to arm ourselves with the Word of God. We faced battles in our regular daily lives, and we wanted to prepare ourselves to win these battles. For me, I wanted to be able to reflexively remember that God commanded me to be self-controlled so I would stop before grabbing that extra handful of pretzels. I wanted to remember that God commanded me to be diligent so I'd get out of bed instead of hitting the snooze button on my alarm clock. I turned the words of the Bible into weapons and wielded them against everyday pitfalls and weaknesses.

In my church, when we read the Bible, we read it as though the history, the context and the purpose of the original writing didn't matter. To us, the Bible was different from any other collection of writings, and there was no need to apply a standard literary analysis to its books. Its words were powerful enough, we thought, that we could extract them from their context, and they would still tell us the truth. This is why we wrote individual verses on index cards, isolated and removed from any consideration of the author's characteristics and interests, cultural context, original audience or original language. The only justification we needed in order to perform these extractions was the self-approval issued by the Bible itself. Hebrews 4:12 says "The word of God is living and active, sharper than any two-edged sword" and II Timothy 3:16 says "all scripture is breathed out by God and profitable for teaching, for re-proof, for correction, and for training in righteousness." I was taught to take these self-declarations seriously and literally, memorizing isolated passages not only because they could keep me safe from life's pitfalls, but for a much greater reason. I believed these words had come directly from the mouth of God.

Biblical living was difficult to accomplish. I knew from my daily Bible reading assignments that these books were filled with poetic language, boring lists with unclear purposes and complicated cultural and historical references that were over my head. But in my church community, we believed that living according to the Bible was the path to a fulfilled earthly life and an eternal heavenly life. We needed a point of access; some way to take these complex texts and distill them into tangible, applicable directives for our daily lives. We believed that, since the Bible was "God-breathed, living and active," that any simple, digestible nugget of wisdom we would extract from it would be a God-breathed nugget of wisdom. Our index card verses declaratively displayed these nuggets of wisdom for us.

The Bible played an important role in our lives: it reminded us that we weren't automatically "in," that God didn't automatically accept us, but that we had to respond to him in order to gain his approval. We had to prove that we were doing our part to honor God.

Philippians 3:18-19 reminded me that I had to resist gluttony and exhibit self-control. Proverbs 31:30 reminded me to avoid vanity and instead focus on fearing the Lord. II Timothy 2:15 told me I had to avoid laziness and maintain resourcefulness and productivity, and that this was the path to becoming a "worker who has no need to be ashamed."

"The Christian life is simple, but it's not easy." I first heard this statement from my pastor, and it became a defining description of the type of Christian faith I tried to cultivate. When it came to food and gluttony, this applied perfectly: restricting my food intake wasn't easy. It felt difficult to let my empty stomach keep growling instead of having a late-night snack. I didn't like eating rice cakes instead of bread and extra broccoli instead of dessert. It annoyed me to record every calorie I ate, and it was frustrating to try to keep my stomach satisfied without exceeding my calorie limits. None of this was easy, but the reasoning behind it was very simple: God would not tolerate being usurped by my stomach. The verses that we amplified the most—the ones that ended up on index cards, posted throughout our house—were those that distilled "godly living" into simple commandments, instructing us to behave in particular ways in order to be accepted by God. Bonus martyr points were given if the simple distillation issued a mandate that was *not* easy to follow.

On my bedroom wall, right next to my glow-in-the-dark DIY northern hemisphere constellation map, was another Bible verse index card, written in my own handwriting. The card read "The heavens declare the glory of God, and the sky above proclaims his handiwork" (Psalm 19:1). As a kid intrigued by science, I thought I knew exactly what this verse meant. In my mind, the verse meant that the natural world reflects God's character. I expected the principles governing nature to be just as concrete and unwavering as God's biblical laws. Scientists don't have to guess at the meanings of principles, laws and relationships in science; scientists can test them. If there's any confusion, the scientific method, given enough time, can eventually resolve it. Scientists make measurements, quantify properties and observe outcomes until the murkiness has been eradicated and the gray areas have been edged back, revealing a clear dividing line between black and white. Although I knew it wouldn't be easy, the formulaic nature of the scientific method always seemed to be simple.

I expected to find definable relationships, logical outcomes and concrete explanations in the natural sciences. When I tell a new acquaintance that I'm a molecular biologist, I receive a consistent reaction: they assume I'm logical. The natural sciences, I'm often told, are for people who like explanations. Scientists become scientists because they like things that "make sense." This reputation is not unfounded; nature obeys laws and follows patterns, and science systematically explores these laws. I never imagined there would be any wiggle room in this world of airtight definitions, cause-effect relationships and predictably obeyed laws.

In my world of Bible verse extraction, memorization and application, science provided the perfect promise of simplicity. It seemed to pair well with the mandates and litmus tests that I had learned to extract from ancient biblical texts. Scientific principles were different from biblical principles, though, evoking none of the anxiety and guilt of my spiritual world. I could assume a more detached perspective when I studied science. Science didn't have the impossibly high stakes of religion, and it didn't ask for any of the complex self-critique that my spirituality required. God's instructions were sources of internal stress. Was I gluttonous when I ate that piece of chocolate? Was it gossip when I told that story about my friend to my mom? Was I grumbling and complaining when I told my mom my math homework was too hard? The principles of the natural sciences, on the other hand, didn't apply to my behavior; they applied to the behavior of things I could observe from a distance; things like cells and molecules. Science promised the simplicity and logic that I loved and the detachment that I needed.

In my evangelical Christian community, we described the Bible as "inerrant," which meant that we believed the Bible to contain fact. Our belief system centered on this assertion and we needed no corroboration other than the Bible's own internal declarations. We believed the entirety of the biblical text, even the anecdotes mentioned seemingly in passing, to be historically and scientifically accurate, containing no errors. We not only treated the Bible like it was a science textbook or a technical document, but a perfect one at that. We believed it could withstand any amount of fact-checking. Partially for our own education and partially for the purpose of convincing non-believers, we learned how to demonstrate the inerrancy of the Bible. I, like so many evangelical kids, was homeschooled in part because of the abundance of homeschool curricula that was written by other evangelicals, which would teach us how to argue for biblical inerrancy. I was specifically taught to approach education with a confirmation bias: any new fact or phenomenon I'd encounter would be passed through the filter of biblical compatibility. If it contradicted a passage in the Bible, we'd reject it. I attended classes, retreats and seminars to learn how to defend and prove my church's doctrines. We were young-earth creationists and we believed that the notion of biological evolution was a lie, fabricated by atheist scientists who were anxious to reject the notion of a creator. I was taught to reject any biological notion that would contradict young-earth creationism. We adhered strictly to the idea that male and female are the only two genders, and that every person's gender matches their biological sex. I was taught to reject any description of human biology or psychology that suggested otherwise. We believed human life to indisputably begin at conception and I was taught to ignore any developmental biologist who tried to introduce nuance to this notion.

We read books presenting pieces of archaeological and biological evidence that happened to support our literal interpretation of the biblical creation poem. When we encountered information that contradicted the biblical texts, we looked for any possible way to invalidate that evidence. The inerrancy of the Bible was such an important cornerstone of our belief system that we'd go to any measure in order to defend it. If any part of the Bible were thought to be false, we believed the verity of the whole thing was under threat.

I thought my faith would fall apart unless I defined it with certainty and clarity. My beliefs had to be airtight. I needed them to stay the same in all cultural and historical contexts. We described these beliefs as "infallible," meaning they could never be wrong. And this was the only type of foundation we thought we could really trust. In fact, in my church community, I was often warned about the danger of trusting any other foundation. To us, these faulty foundations were the ones Jesus warned us about in the parable of the house built on sand (Matthew 7:24-27). Unsteady and unstable, prone to rapid and unpredictable shifting and by no means fit to serve as a foundation upon which to build. We could never build our faith on anything that would change in response to its context; we needed solid ground. This was the definition of "truth" to us: truth would never change, but it would stay exactly the same no matter the context.

Our belief in the Bible's inerrancy merged with our

belief in its infallibility to produce the summation of our biblical interpretation method: literalism. For us, biblical literalism meant deliberate adherence to the primary, strict meanings of biblical passages, rather than their figurative or metaphorical meanings. It meant that extracting verses from their context was actually preferred over considering the purpose, original intent and cultural significance of the writing. I was taught that to treat the Bible as literally true was a sign of respect for these texts. We were convinced that any metaphorical meaning could distract or even deceive us, and that treating the meaning as figurative would water it down. In our minds, reading the Bible as a collection of metaphors and figures of speech would be a cop-out, the kind of cheap trick that sinners use to justify their sin.

"The Christian life is simple, but it's not easy." At first, it really did seem simple. In the early days of my weight loss efforts, as a 12-year-old trying to do what God asked of me, I believed in monolithic, unchanging truth. This kind of truth is incredibly simple. What a relief, I thought, that I'd always know the answers beforehand. No matter the life situations I'd encounter, as long as I remained equipped with a rich memory bank of Bible verses, I'd know how to manage any situation in the way God desired. We believed that those people who filtered, contextualized and watered down the Bible were hiding from the truth and ultimately were removing themselves further from God. In our own eyes, we, the Christians who believed the Bible to be inerrant, infallible and literal, were honoring God's word by simply applying truth, rather than interpreting it.

Inevitably, the simplicity of my young faith didn't last long. In fact, the Bible quickly began to confuse me. Although the concept of permanent, monolithic truth is indeed simple, the actual mandates were not cut-and-dry. The real-life situations I had to navigate were confusing and complicated. For instance, if I ate seven chips after lunch, did that mean I was making my stomach "my god," the danger warned against in Philippians 3? What if I planned on it ahead of time? What if I was really hungry when I ate those chips? If I only hit the snooze button once, did that mean I was lazy, or would I have had to hit the button multiple times to qualify as lazy? What if I was extra tired that morning? What if I had trouble falling asleep the night before? What if I hadn't hit the snooze button any other days that week? If I really liked another girl's shoes and thought to myself that I wanted a pair like hers, did that mean I was covetous? Did it mean I was vain if I particularly liked the way I looked on a certain day? If I wished I had trendier clothes, did that mean I was greedy? What if I earned money for them and bought them? Was that still selfish and frivolous?

For every biblical mandate, I saw only two possibilities: good and bad. I could either be gluttonous or self-controlled; lazy or diligent; productive or fruitless; conceited or humble. Godliness and sinfulness were the only two possibilities and they were mutually exclusive polar opposites. In my real daily living, however, the dividing lines between these two possibilities were rarely clear. Instead, I encountered blurred gray areas, and these gray areas only grew larger over time, spreading wider and wider with every experience I had.

When I first started to learn about genetics, I thought I knew what to expect. It seemed like a puzzle. DNA, my textbooks explained, is a code, a blueprint that gives detailed instructions for building a functioning cell. Of course, those cells build organs, organisms and eventually, if enough of them are working with each other, people.

Genetics seemed to be an ideal example of a logical science, providing concrete explanations for human traits. The influence of genes is strong and precise enough to produce inherited traits, explaining not only general characteristics like my blue eyes, but even finer details. My genes are responsible for the shape of my eyelids, for instance, which squeeze into a squinty smile, looking strikingly similar to my grandmother's and my father's. It can be predicted, on the basis of a person's genetic code, what their tendencies are toward developing particular diseases, or their risks of passing inherited diseases to their children. Genes seem to be absolutes, clearly defining life in terms of molecules. Genetics seems to be the key to demystifying human existence.

Genetics is certainly a complex science, and it's not easy to learn its rules, but the science itself is highly systematic. All we have to do in order to understand DNA is learn to read its code. Genes, I learned, correspond with traits, and DNA can be decoded by tracing genes directly to traits. Once the basic laws of genetics are known, the traits of an organism can be determined and its characteristics predicted unambiguously. Genes, from my perspective as a young scientist, did not seem to be open to interpretation, but seemed to be absolutes. I thought genes had concrete, precise meanings which remain unchanged, regardless of context.

I wanted my beliefs about God to have meanings that were just as precise as the meanings of the genes in my DNA molecules. Just as human genes translate into human traits, I wanted my beliefs to translate into behaviors. I wanted my beliefs to be more than simple mental assertions, but I wanted them to function as my instructions for living. The Bible, to me and to my fellow churchgoers whom I so deeply respected, was an unquestionable monolithic authority. I believed the Bible to be a complete collection of absolutes. My own interpretations of scripture were the laws of my universe, the codes that dictated my system of beliefs, priorities and thought patterns. My beliefs had out-comes, taking up residence in my thought patterns, my self-perception, my relationships, my habits and even my body. My beliefs could send me into cold panicky sweats, guilt-ridden and ashamed when I fell short of the behaviors those beliefs prescribed. On the other hand, my beliefs could bring me a warm swell of pride when I followed their man-dates. They were now authoritative entities of their own; the prescriptions and standards of my faith wielded power over my thought patterns, my emotions, my behaviors and my self-perception.

When I made the Bible my monolithic authority, it quickly became an unlimited, unchecked ruler, never to be questioned, filtered or doubted. It was a harsh master, de-claring that private sins like gluttony were significant enough to warrant eternal hell. My belief provided fertile ground for obsession and compulsion to flourish, unhin-dered. Ridding myself of sin, no matter how petty and in-consequential that sin might be, seemed to be my only worthwhile pursuit, and when I succumbed to anything I considered to be sin, it resulted in overwhelming guilt. I be-lieved that in God's eyes, there was no difference between private sins and sins that profoundly damage our commu-nities. All sin, according to my church's teachings, would be punished with eternal hellfire. I was taught to worship, love and pray to a God who would punish me for occasional overeating just the same as he would punish a murderer. Monolithic truth left no wiggle room, no allowance for ex-ceptions and no grace when I fell short.

Over time, I learned to do the only logical thing, given that I believed the stakes were so high. When I wasn't sure how best to interpret a biblical passage, I took the high road. I assumed the most conservative and restrictive interpreta-tion to be true. My eternal destiny was on the line. I couldn't afford to take risks. If I wasn't quite sure whether or not my eating habits were gluttonous, I would still pray for forgiveness, just to be safe. I'd repent and promise God that I'd never be gluttonous again. The line between gluttony and normal eating is difficult to define, so I simply kept trying to eat less and less food, and especially, to eat less enjoyable food. In my mind, every cookie I decided not to eat, every meal I diligently recorded in my food diary, and every plain salad I chose not to cover with ranch dressing was a step toward godliness, not just a step toward my weight loss goal. Denying myself, even in these simple and everyday ways was, I'd been taught, what God wanted me to do.

By the end of high school, I settled into a much more comfortable and healthy weight. My blood pressure was normal, my cholesterol was fine and my doctor was no longer concerned. Although I no longer kept a food diary, I could never forget about Philippians 3. Even if I wanted to forget, a belief this dramatic in a God this harsh doesn't fall away easily. It wasn't just Philippians 3, but it was all the other verses and passages as well. The index cards, the Sunday school memory verses and the daily Bible study produced their intended outcomes. I couldn't forget Proverbs 31:30, Philippians 2:14, Psalm 48, Philippians 4:13 or II Timothy 2:16. I read these as mandates delivered directly from God, that set a standard of behavior that would be completely free of vanity, laziness, anxiety, and inefficiency.

Each day was a cycle that began with aspirational resolutions and ended with guilt. I'd start every morning with a resolution to eat less, use my time wisely and avoid selfishness. I set the bar so high that it was usually no more than an hour later that I'd disappoint myself, realizing I'd given in to my hunger, jealousy, angry thoughts, ungratefulness or laziness. I'd repent, promising my authoritative God that I'd change my ways, but the cycle would inevitably repeat. I'd rationalize my eating habits, my thoughts and my use of my time, but I'd always find a reason to doubt those rationalizations and maintain a deep self-suspicion, worried that

God would punish me for my unconfessed sins.

By my early twenties, my desire to do what God wanted me to do had transformed into a crippling self-hatred. No matter what I did, I could always find a way that, by some biblical standard, I wasn't following God's mandates.

It only took a few years of young adulthood before I found that, contradictory to my pastor's declaration, this particular Christian life was anything but simple. In fact, it was impossibly complicated and confusing. Calling the Christian life "simple" had pushed me into a downward spiral of desperate attempts, failures and self-hatred.

The downward spiral didn't alarm me, though. In fact, I took it as a sign that I was on the right track. I believed that the Christian life was inherently difficult, so I oddly counted my self-hatred, anxiety and obsession as evidence that I was faithfully living this Christian life. I'd been taught that everything within me was sinful, so the fact that I experienced inner turmoil was, in a twisted way, an encouraging sign that I was successfully suppressing my sinful nature. If my daily living was comfortable, I'd convinced myself, that would be a sign that I was living in sin.

Over time, though, biblical literalism produced more than just inner turmoil. It produced an ideological challenge. In my family and my church, we believed that Bible study was the best way to strengthen our beliefs. Bible discussions were important components of church services, youth group meetings and family dinner table conversations. Bible study was a component of my family's home-school curriculum, and I was assigned to read biblical texts on a daily basis, as well as biblical commentaries and study guides that bolstered our literalist doctrines. These biblical studies, discussions and debates had one single objective: reaching a more accurate and godly interpretation of the Bible. I was never interested in proving my correctness or winning a debate when it came to biblical scholarship. In God's eyes, I believed, it didn't matter whether or not I won an argument; it mattered that I was faithful to the biblical text. I could win an argument and still not be interpreting the Bible accurately and faithfully. When I disagreed with someone in my family or church about the meaning of a scripture passage, I saw it as a warning sign that at least one of us was gravely and dangerously wrong. Disagreements were problems to be solved and errors to be corrected. I believed scripture to be infallible, so conflicts and discrepancies left me no option but to blame the faulty human interpretations that had been applied to the texts. Confusion was always the fault of the reader.

This was the reason my own confusion was so alarming to me — and I had a lot of confusion. Not only was I confused about the Bible, but at least some of that confusion seemed to be baked right into the biblical texts themselves. For instance, in the gospel of Mark, Jesus is asked to share his opinion of someone who is allegedly working in the name of Christ, but who neglects to give credit to Christ. He responds with a generous declaration, "For the one who is not against us is for us" (Mark 9:40). But in the book of Matthew, one of the other gospel accounts, Jesus seems to change his stance, taking a much stricter approach. He faces criticism, with some observers accusing him of using demonic power to drive out demons. Here he defends himself, responding much more harshly: "Whoever is not with me is against me" (Matt. 12:30). So, which is it? Would it be enough to simply not be against Jesus, or does a person have to explicitly claim they're with him in order to be counted as one of his followers? Would my neighbors, the ones who never talked about getting saved, who didn't talk about reading the Bible every day and who didn't pray in tongues — would they still be counted as followers of Christ, just because they weren't specifically and outspokenly against Christ? I'd been taught to use the texts of the Bible as standards, ways of determining which behaviors and beliefs were pleasing to God and which were unacceptable. Passages like these, however, were making it seem that Jesus himself might not have been sure of the standards.

I responded to this confusion in the only way that seemed reasonable, given the fact my eternal fate was on the line: I drew the most conservative conclusions I could draw. Why risk finding out whether or not I have to explicitly declare myself a follower of Christ? Better to boldly and openly declare myself "with" Christ. That way I'd have nothing to worry about.

Drawing these conservative conclusions didn't free me from anxiety. I still wondered if my declarations of godliness would be heartfelt enough for God to accept them. Would God consider me a follower of Christ, even though I had plenty of moments in my day when Christ was the furthest thing from my mind? Every biblical mandate pushed me a little further into a spiral of anxiety.

By interpreting the Bible literally, we were treating it as though it were a scientific text. We believed that the Bible's declarations were universal laws, such as "for all have sinned and fall short of the glory of God" (Romans 3:23), and "God loves a cheerful giver" (II Corinthians 9:7). I was taught to interpret the Bible, written and recorded long before the development of the scientific method, as though its complex poetic, historically and culturally influenced language was equivalent to methodically and systematically developed scientific content.

There was a difference, of course, between biblical laws and scientific laws. Biblical laws mandated the personal, private aspects of my life, but I was detached from scientific laws. When it came to science, I was an observer occupying a rather uninvolved vantage point. Biblical laws, on the other hand, were mandates regarding my own behavior. Natural laws, which governed the behaviors of unthinking and unconscious cells and molecules, induced none of the anxiety and obsession that the Bible created.

The field of genetics, like any science, is a work in progress. Studying the natural sciences is like looking at a painting that's only partially completed. It was easy to overlook this as a student who watched articulate professors draw intricately detailed reaction mechanisms on chalkboards and who read definitive statements written in boldface type in biology textbooks. In graduate school, though, my glossy textbook pages which displayed hand-selected examples and easy-to-understand diagrams were replaced with articles from scientific journals. I was beginning to gradually realize what science really investigates: the transforming, progressing, ever-expanding, never-fully-pinned-down aspects of reality. This approach to investigating a reality that resists simple absolutes would deeply alter the way I made sense of what I observed in the laboratory as well as the way I approached my spirituality.

Many aspects of genetics fall squarely within this category of never-fully-pinned-down realities. Mysteries certainly abound, and many of them seem far too complex to ever be fully predictable or even traceable. One genetic mystery, a particularly confounding problem, was thoroughly investigated by a group of research biologists (Duhl 1994). The problem they addressed was a phenomenon that seemed to break all the rules, and the more I learned about it, the more elusive its explanation seemed to become.

The subject of the research study was a specific type of mouse, the agouti mouse. Agouti mice exhibit incredible diversity in their appearances. Members of the same genetic lineage, even littermates, can appear dramatically different from one another. They can range widely in adult sizes, over a much broader size spectrum than typical mouse lineages. Their coloring can be brown, yellow, red or a mott-led in-between combination of these. When this group of bi-ologists started tackling the problem of agouti mice, there didn't seem to be any means of predicting the appearance of any one agouti mouse. Their appearances seemed to be determined randomly. Even genetically identical mice might appear drastically different from one another, with no apparent causal factors linked to their individual appear-ances.

I imagine that the scientists assumed they would dis-cover some mutated or deleted gene, or some undiscovered genetic aberration causing the mice to appear so drastically different from one another, despite their identical genetic codes. Traits don't just appear without a genetic basis, so the biologists set out to identify the cause of the differences. They chose three littermates, one small and brown, one large and yellow and one mottled and medium-sized. The first thing they did was identify the specific sequence of nu-cleotides in the three genomes, cracking their genetic codes. What they found when they sequenced the mouse genomes, however, took them even further away from an explanation for their distinct appearances: the three mice had identical genomes.

Sometimes in scientific investigation, there are pieces of data that I imagine a scientist might wish they hadn't dis-covered. Some facts are so confounding that I imagine the scientist hopes that they made a mistake. Admitting a mis-take to colleagues seems easier than explaining seemingly impossible data to the entire science community. This ge-nomic sequence data — the fact that all three mice had iden-tical DNA sequences — seems to be one such problematic finding. These biologists had a profound challenge: they had to explain traits that do *not* correspond precisely to genes.

Middle school biology textbooks typically describe genes as blueprints. Genes are said to be codes; highly detailed sets of instructions, foundational plans for building human beings. Genes are transcribed into mRNA transcripts, which are then translated into proteins: the building blocks of human traits. Genes form the logical, rational foundation, even for realities as diverse, multifaceted and complex as earthly life forms. This process of **transcription** and **translation,** by which a gene produces a protein is called **gene expression**. We could spend multiple semester-long courses learning the details of these processes (as well as learning about the overwhelming number of details that remain unexplained), but the most important thing to know is that it's a cellular interpretation system. In fact, many of the terms that are used to describe and define gene expression, including "transcription" and "translation" are borrowed from linguistics.

Proteins, the final products of gene expression, are constructed through a series of tightly controlled cooperative processes inside the cell. DNA is analogous to a text that, when interpreted, produces concrete, measurable and identifiable protein products. Unlike the murky, messy world of interpreting human written and spoken language, cells operate according to strict laws. The unthinking and unconscious nature of cell machinery seems to free the gene expression process from the capacity for error that we encounter in our human lives. Cells do not make choices the way humans do, and thus do not run the risk of choosing poorly. I was taught that I'm always in danger of applying my own interpretation to the truths I read in the Bible, but cells don't run this risk. Cells accomplish a remarkably precise type of interpretation.

The precision and tight regulation inherent in gene expression makes the problem of agouti mice seem even more difficult to solve. Genetics, when its rules are followed healthily, doesn't seem like it could contain wiggle room or imprecision, but these three agouti mice seemed to provide an unquestionable example of wiggle room, plain for the eye to see.

The researchers looked for explanations in a subfield of genetics: epigenetics. Epigenetics is the investigation of every aspect of genetics that is *not* included in the genetic code. Epigenetic forces function like dimmer switches, modulating gene expression up or down. The concept of epigenetics is based on an understanding that the cell machinery doesn't simply *read* a gene. There is a complex process of *interpretation* involved in transcribing and translating a gene, and this interpretation process is regulated by a concert of forces. These forces—the epigenetic regulatory factors—make up the gene's context.

The appearances of the agouti mice—which were strikingly distinct, of course—were traced to one single gene, a gene which had been previously identified and named the agouti gene. Of course, this gene's sequence (like all the gene sequences in the three mouse genomes) was identical among all three mice. Finding no distinction at the genetic level, the biologists moved on to consider the epigenetic level.

Epigenetic factors range so widely that they are challenging to define. The factors can be chemical, physical or mechanical. Chemicals, either on the interior or exterior of the cell, can be part of the epigenetic landscape. These chemicals may originate as by-products of the processes occurring inside cells, or they may be taken in as part of the mouse's diet, inhaled in the air the mouse breathes or swallowed in the water it drinks. Epigenetic differences can be time-dependent, produced by physiological changes that occur over time. Gene expression efficiency can decrease with age, degrading cell components. Spatial differences can impact epigenetics, such as the specific orientation of the DNA molecule inside the cell. These factors, largely unpredictable and often untraceable, produce effects that seem haphazard, although molecular forces are at work in every step. On cellular interiors, complexity masquerades as chaos. Each step is simple, but simplicity piled layer after layer upon simplicity creates mind-boggling complexity.

The diversity of epigenetic factors means that there are multiple dimmer switches that can all affect one or many genes simultaneously in ways that produce synergistic cellular effects. Epigenetic factors may have different affinities for multiple genes and therefore may affect those genes differently based on their genetic neighbors and the abundance or strength of the specific epigenetic factor. It's stunning how complex the collective effects of epigenetic factors can be, diverse categories of forces compounding with one another, interacting and intertwining in complex orchestration. These dimmer switches, with their multifaceted origins, influences and impacts, are powerful enough to modulate gene expression over a tremendously broad range of possibilities.

In fact, the range of possibilities, in the case of the agouti gene, is broad enough to produce wildly diverse appearances in genetically identical mice. There is a chemical process that heavily regulates agouti gene expression. This process is called methylation, the physical attachment of methyl chemical groups to a gene. These methyl groups can directly block transcription, preventing production of the agouti gene's protein product. The more methyl groups attach to the gene, the less frequently the gene gets transcribed and translated into the protein it encodes. We find parallels here between the complicated effects of epigenetics and the diversity of theological understandings, filtered by our cultural and social contexts.

Over time, biologists have demonstrated that the color and size of an agouti mouse correlates singularly with the number of methyl groups that are attached to the agouti gene (Dolinoy 2008). Methylation, a process that does not change the genetic code, but only changes the way the code is interpreted, is powerful enough to create the difference between a giant yellow mouse and a tiny brown mouse.

Methyl group attachment is controlled by a variety of factors that are so wide-ranging and sensitive that they seem unrelated and unpredictable. The degree of methylation depends on factors like the mouse's diet, activity level, and the mother's diet during her pregnancy. These factors create the chemical environment of the agouti gene; they comprise its context, and the context has the ability to wholly transform the gene's manifestation.

As a young science student, I expected to learn that genes are absolute; that they create concrete, direct and predictable outcomes. In reality, genes are like the colorful confetti pieces at the end of a kaleidoscope. The color and shape of each piece stays the same, no matter how you turn the chamber of the kaleidoscope. Although those pieces never change, they pass through an intricate system of mirrors, and the outcome is that they are arranged in any one of ostensibly infinite patterns. Their transformations are mesmerizing. As the chamber turns and the patterns undergo their dynamic transformations, each colorful, eye-catching pattern is so different from the one that came before that it's hard to believe they're all just different representations of the same basic material.

Genes are not monolithic predictors, but rather they define possibilities. Their outcomes shift over a vast array, transformed by their context. Although there is such great elasticity in the products of genetic codes, there is still an absoluteness underlying their diversity of expression. The transcription and translation of the agouti gene remain unaltered regardless of its degree of methylation, even though the timing, cell type, rate and frequency of those reactions modulate dramatically in response to methylation. Every context and every lived experience will transform even identical genetic codes in ways that render drastically distinct outcomes. It's not the simple, airtight, precise and predictable world I once expected.

It is possible for something to be true but not precise;

constant but not fixed; explicit yet still elastic. In fact, this type of truth—the type that has the ability to shift, every context transforming its meaning—has a power and beauty that I couldn't imagine when I believed all truth to be static, monolithic and unchanging. This dynamic kind of truth is wisdom that clothes itself in response to its environment. The truth that is seen through a kaleidoscope produces compounding variety. It generates infinite diversity from a finite underlying reality.

As an evangelical kid, I believed my task was to define and strengthen the boundaries of truth. I thought the truth needed to be preserved. I wanted to be able to state my claimed-by-faith beliefs in clear and concise terms. As my faith matured, I thought I'd learn more precisely how to live—what, when and how much to eat, when and how long to rest, what type of work to do, what daily activities to prioritize. My goal, the sign of strong faith would be to clearly know the behaviors, attitudes and priorities that would determine whether I was godly or sinful; whether I was in God's kingdom or outside of it.

I spent vast amounts of my energy as a young evangelical trying to ensure my place in the "godly" category. By directing my energy inward and scrutinizing my own behaviors, I overlooked the deep wisdom in the Christian spiritual tradition. A rich, deep message of wisdom is present, even in the Bible passage I used as the basis for my self-obsession. The person described in Philippians 3:18-19 is wholly focused on their stomach. This inwardly focused person misses out on opportunities to love—or even pay attention to—their neighbors. Isn't this the greatest cost of living as though your "god is your stomach?" Rather than living in anxious fear of going to hell for eating an arbitrary number of chips, how much more fruitful could my efforts be if I focused instead on enjoying my life, my work and my relationships with others? For me, avoiding sin became an obstacle to enjoying the richness of my own spiritual tradition.

What if, instead, I approach biblical wisdom with an understanding of the power of contextual interpretation? Genes, the fundamental originators of traits, pass through an epigenetic interpretation system, so what if I assume that biblical truth passes through an interpretation system of its own: social structures, communal values and technological possibilities? What if I search for the underlying truth, the foundational truth that rests beneath these multifaceted layers of interpretation? This approach leads me deeper into the heart of spiritual wisdom, and away from investing my energy in obsessive self-scrutiny. When I see scripture through this lens, I begin to look beyond the directives and mandates at the surface, in search of the enduring truth that undergirds them.

When considering how the agouti gene is interpreted by a mouse's cells, the only incorrect analysis would be an exclusive, precise and simple definition of the gene's outcome. To say the agouti gene produces brown fur is correct, but to say the agouti gene produces *only* brown fur is incorrect. To say the agouti gene produces yellow fur is correct, but to say it *only* produces yellow fur is incorrect. Instead of searching for a way to clearly and precisely define these truths, our most appropriate approach is to search for ways to expand them. Our search for truth becomes less about preserving a concisely defined mandate and more about imagining the ways deep wisdom could be transformed in order to be meaningful in our current context.

There was a time when I thought the end goal of genetics was to demystify life. I thought the aim was to simplify the complex traits of an organism or a cell or a person, finding a gene for every trait. I thought we could isolate genes, extract them from their context and still know exactly which traits they would create. Epigenetics shows how futile it is to attempt this type of simplification. To isolate a gene, apart from the epigenetic factors that regulate its expression, would be such an oversimplification that it would be a misrepresentation. Epigenetic factors—the various chemical groups that intermittently attach and detach from a gene, the cell components that cause DNA to spool in one orientation versus another inside a cell—change the way that a gene is interpreted. These factors are lenses, filters, reflectors and refiners. They're the complex system of interdependent lenses through which the gene passes before it creates reality.

It makes more sense to talk about what a gene *renders* than what a gene *is*. A gene's impacts are so foundational, and they underlie reality so deeply that they are unpredictable unless we have the entire picture in our view; that is, unless we're able to consider the full intricate landscape of epigenetic effects. Philippians 3:18-19 is one rendering of spiritual wisdom. But it is only one passage of a letter written from one man's perspective to a specific group of people at a particular point in time. These words were written by an author who had a particular relationship with his readers. There was a cultural context, undoubtedly including understandings and suppositions that are not familiar to me in my modern cultural context, and are not explicit in the text. To ignore this context would be such an oversimplification that it would be a misrepresentation. It would be a mistreatment of this text to treat these words as a universal directive, applicable as an isolated, literal mandate that reaches across time and space. When we read the Bible, we're eavesdropping on conversations that never included us and which we have no reason to assume were intended for us. We will easily misconstrue these words if we don't interrogate their context.

What I was not taught as a young evangelical is that I will always see through a lens of some sort. I always interpret what I read and hear. As a modern white American, I'm not often asked to acknowledge my perspective. I'm not accustomed to differentiating myself from my neighbors because I live in a society in which my identity is prioritized and privileged. Nonetheless, I am always interpreting what I see, hear and read, as we all are, and my interpretations can radically transform my understanding of passages like Philippians 3:18-19. Acknowledging my own lens is the first step toward embracing and honoring, rather than resisting, the capacity of foundational truths to transform throughout a variety of contexts.

Jesus, in those oddly contradictory passages in Mark and Matthew, is asked to categorize people according to an unwavering, context-independent standard. He replies with a declaration that the question lacked validity: he provides answers that change according to the situation. When I first read these passages in the gospels, I was troubled. I believed God's truth was unwavering and independent of context. I stuck to strict categorization because I couldn't imagine a world where truth would be anything but monolithic. That's why I chose to play it safe and take the more conservative approach anytime I could. I'd rather risk being too harsh than too lax, because erring on the side of a liberal interpretation could be enough to seal my eternal fate in hell.

If I look deeper, though, I become open to the possibility that Jesus was doing something radical in these conversations. It seems that he's rejecting the very structure of mutually exclusive, strictly defined categories. He's talking about the kind of truth that can transform; the kind of truth that passes through contextual interpretation systems and manifests differently in various circumstances. He refuses to concisely define his followers. He offers no generalized rubric for categorizing people as his followers or his opposition, but instead reveals the irrelevance of these generalized categories. He's tearing apart the very premise that truth can be isolated from its context and preserved, free of interpretation.

To extract biblical verses from their cultural and historical context, and from the context of the surrounding passages, would be like extracting a gene from its epigenetic context. The gene cannot be meaningfully translated or interpreted until it takes on the nuance of epigenetic context. The text has no meaning until it takes on the nuance of real-life experiential context. The text is just words, until the word becomes flesh.

We account for this nuance first by searching for common ground. The biologists studying agouti mice could have focused on the surface-level differences in appearance among the three mice, completely missing the underlying unifying factor. The agouti gene is the unifying factor, forming the foundation of all three mice. Epigenetics — the context of the gene — creates enough nuance, difference, variation and diversity to produce these three mice who, on the surface, appear to have nothing in common.

We could spend our spiritual lives focusing on the distinctions that appear on the surface. We could focus on differences in behavior, trying to clearly draw dividing lines between godliness and sinfulness. Am I gluttonous or self-controlled? Am I vain or conceited? Am I lazy or productive? Any one of these questions could keep us obsessively occupied for an entire lifetime. But just as these biologists searched for an underlying reality that runs deeper than apparent differences, we can search for underlying realities that run much deeper than behaviors and surface-level attributes.

There are truth claims that should raise our suspicion. The more precise and specific a truth claim, the more ardently we should seek to expand it. Just as a biologist would be wise to question a statement such as "the agouti gene only generates brown fur," we would be wise to question exclusive and limiting truth claims. The more contextual factors a claim excludes, the more insistently we should ask why. If we want to honestly engage with an underlying truth, we must first understand the arbitrary specificity of our experience and seek to identify and understand our lenses, thus allowing our perspective to expand. As a result, we will invite and include more and more manifestations of truth.

A prediction made on the basis of genetics alone usually requires vast oversimplification and complete ignorance of the dramatic power of epigenetics. Likewise, prescriptive truth claims are usually oversimplifications of the underlying wisdom they claim to represent. While the behaviors prescribed may not be detrimental, their exclusivity and the shame that comes from failing to adhere to them will almost certainly be detrimental. The oppression and trauma I've observed in my religious communities have typically stemmed from insistent adherence to prescriptive truth claims.

It's not that prescriptive, precise manifestations of truth are always wrong, it's simply that they only represent a portion of reality. They will certainly be correct in some situations. However, when we exclusively adhere to these manifestations, we weaken the truth that underlies them. And not only is it a weakening, but it can be a source of oppression and trauma for those who do not or cannot fit into our tightly defined category of godliness.

Treating all truth as monolithic not only fostered my self-hatred; it caused me to completely miss the point. The goal of engaging with truth is to keep turning the kaleidoscope. The point is to allow underlying truths to keep evolving, transforming and progressing toward greater inclusion. Life, in all of its forms, from the most concrete biological forms to the abstract spiritual form, is defined by *transformation*. A gene's expression is different for every cell containing it. It's always changing through lived experience, and it's transformed by context. If I approach spiritual truth in this way, I become more and more enthralled with its beauty and depth, and less obsessed with my own self-scrutiny.

Having now seen that my experience of truth and reality is silently shaped by my lenses, I am left with a choice: I can allow myself to be consumed with anxiety and shame in the times when I suspect that my image of truth must change in order to encompass a fixed reality, or I can celebrate the beauty of the unfolding truth that emerges as I turn the kaleidoscope. It's a choice I must make every day. I have found that when I turn the kaleidoscope, the truth is deep enough and strong enough to keep shifting, transforming and progressing. And I cannot help but be transformed with it.

4

BEARING FRUIT

I wedged the pillow beneath my rib cage so it propped me up. I was positioned so the slowly unspooling cassette tape was right at my eye level. The black tape unwound from the left side, gradually accumulating on the right-hand spool. I would have my 11th birthday later that year, and even though I wouldn't be allowed to officially join youth group until I turned 13, my parents agreed it would be appropriate for me to listen to the tapes from the youth group retreat. There were several reasons I wanted to listen. First, I was the youngest of four and always anxious to feel like I fit in with my older siblings. Second, my parents were the featured guest speakers at the retreat. Finally, I couldn't imagine a subject matter that could possibly be more fascinating. That year's youth group retreat was focused on the topic of relationships. In our particular branch of evangelical Christianity, we believed that God had a specific plan for the ways we would live our daily lives. This plan included our relationships. We said that we were building the Kingdom of God, and we believed our relationships with one another were important components of this Kingdom. The Kingdom of God would have its own social structure.

The youth group retreat teachings focused on one particular type of relationship: courtship. The term *courtship* was intentionally chosen in an effort to make it clear that as Christians, we were doing things differently from the rest of the world. This wasn't the same as dating. Even though the messages I received from my family and church about "biblical courtship" differed from messages about romance in popular culture, I could tell there was a universal agreement among all sources. From Bible passages to pop songs to films to the *Babysitters' Club* novels I devoured, the message was the same: it was important that I find a romantic partner in my future. Britney Spears lyrics told me a boyfriend would be all I'd ever need, and the core of my church's message about femininity, romance and relationships—that God created me for the purpose of being partnered with a man—wasn't all that different.

Although romantic relationships were certainly the most intriguing kind to me as a preteen completely awash with hormones, they were by no means the only important relationships for us as Christians. Growing up evangelical, the importance of human relationships had always been emphasized. Evangelism was an essential expression of our faith, and evangelism involves building some sort of relationship with a person. Building our people skills, developing our conversation skills, and refining our leadership skills were such important aspects of our lives that they may as well have been spiritual practices for us. Our churches were built out of human relationships, and we believed the Kingdom of God included a new model for relationships of all kinds.

As I had three siblings in their teens and early twenties, most of the material from my parents' teachings at the weekend retreat was already familiar to me. I'd overheard enough conversations at home to know my family's dating rules. And because the rules were so familiar, I gave them little attention and certainly no resistance. The rules included: dating is always between a male and a female, and the male always does the pursuing. No dating was allowed unless both the male and female could marry within a year in practical terms, so high school relationships were never permitted. In fact, my family's rule was that a relationship should only last for six months before marriage would be discussed. If marriage was still impractical at that point, the relationship must end. No kissing, no touching, no hand-holding and certainly no sex before the wedding. I accepted the rules, and rebellion seemed like the most reckless and foolish form of independence. I never dreamed that I could possibly know better than the adults in my church. I simply wasn't the type to challenge authority, and beyond that, the youth group and college kids I knew in my church—the ones I respected and admired so much—never seemed to question or challenge the rules either.

The part on the cassette tape that really caught my attention was the teaching given only to young women. I'd heard phrases like "biblical femininity," "submission" and "Proverbs 31 woman" regularly in church, but as a younger girl, this language always seemed abstract. I'd never really thought about these terms as applied to me. Now, in the context of the romantic relationships that were so newly intriguing to me as a 12-year-old, biblical femininity started to seem relevant to me.

We believed that sacrifice and submission were included in every Christian's duty. The cross of Christ, to us, was an image of sacrifice, a symbol from God that selflessness, submission and surrender are virtues to which we should all aspire. All Christians were taught to submit to biblical wisdom and to church leadership. There was, however, an additional type of submission expected of female Christians. I was taught that the Kingdom of God is hierarchical and that authority flows from God to church leaders, all of whom were male, then to male church members, and from these male Christians to female Christians. The basis of this structure was Ephesians 5, a letter written by the Apostle Paul to a specific church for reasons that my church never seemed to interrogate. The fact this passage was included in the biblical text was all the rationale we required in order to use it as the basis of our own church structure.

My church taught that a man should submit to the biblical text—over which he himself had interpretive power— but a woman should submit to the plans, goals, desires and values of the man who functioned as the head of her household. These forms of submission are fundamentally different; submitting to biblical texts is not the same as submitting to a person. These taped youth group retreat teachings were my first real introduction to the specialized submission that was expected of me as a female.

It was not only in the context of church leadership that I was taught God had designed a gender-specific hierarchy. Women, I was taught, have a fundamental God-given role that is distinct from that of a man, rooted in our beliefs about the earliest moments of human existence. We treated the creation poem at the beginning of the biblical book of Genesis as though it was the literal scientific documentation of the earliest moments of the existence of the universe. In Genesis, Eve is described as a "help-meet" for Adam. God created Adam first, the creation story describes, and then made Eve out of spare parts from Adam's body. My church community treated this story as a paradigm for the roles of all females. I was taught that women were created to be complementary additions to men.

Gender roles, we believed, would pave the ultimate path to cooperation. We were taught that a clear system of organization—in which the leaders and followers are classified according to gender—would minimize opportunities for conflict. In a sense, it worked, as I never heard a woman in my church challenge or question male authority. Minimizing conflict, however, came at a cost. The pattern of male leadership and female submission was, in function, a hierarchical system of control.

The concept that the world is hierarchical and that I am inherently subordinate didn't seem degrading when I was an adolescent. My church—which encompassed the entirety of my regular social sphere—was structured according to this hierarchy. Male leadership of subordinated females was all that I saw around me and it seemed to be working. I saw my own parents, and other couples of all ages and stages of life whose marriages seemed to operate according to this hierarchy and who seemed to have happy, committed marriages. I heard wives talk about "obeying" their husbands, "serving" their husbands and asking their husbands for "permission," and I never detected resentful tones in these comments. Beyond that, the concept of female subordination felt oddly comforting. It explained any feelings of lack or insufficiency that I had developed. When I doubted myself, or I lacked the bravery or boldness to follow my internal instincts, I could tell myself that it was appropriate for me to remain quiet and submissive and defer to male leadership. I finally had something to blame for any sense of inadequacy that I felt. There's no comfort as warm and welcoming as that of a scapegoat.

The Kingdom of God—the new social structure we were building, with its codes of conduct that we meticulously defended using biblical passages—was predicated on a belief that people have distinct, specialized roles dictated by gender, and for the system to function efficiently, these roles must be organized in a hierarchical fashion. For us, gender was a straightforward way to determine where each person fit into the social structure. Gender told us who was a leader and who was a follower. Passages of ancient biblical texts, written thousands of years ago in patriarchal cultures, were all the support we needed for our conclusions. In retrospect, it was certainly no coincidence that the people interpreting these biblical texts, dictating a gender-based hierarchy and governing our church, were exclusively male.

The injustice of it wouldn't occur to me for many years. At the time, hierarchical organization seemed to be the only means of promoting cooperation and unity. It sounded like the perfect solution to disconnected, inefficient self-serving individuality. A gender-based hierarchical social structure seemed healthy, a system that would eliminate the type of self-serving independence that ultimately damages a community.

Not only did a carefully organized social structure seem healthy, it seemed natural. Order seems to be inherent in everything that occupies our universe, from planets to insects to cells to eyeballs. Each part of every one of these systems has a role to play. The roots of an apple tree have a role to play, and if they fail to fulfill that role, the entire system suffers. The bark of that same tree has a completely different role to play, and although it's distinct, that role is just as vital as that of the roots.

There is a striking difference, however, between natural cellular communities and the social structure that my church community described as the Kingdom of God. Communities of cells contain no leaders and they contain no followers. There is no hierarchical chain of command, no central boss, and there are no overseers. Animals, human bodies and plants function on the basis not of hierarchy but of constant mutual sensitivity and reciprocity. Cellular communities achieve common goals by way of what can only be described as cooperation. Potential dangers are sensed and avoided through a communal effort and warnings of threats are transmitted through the cellular community by way of an intercellular mode of communication. When trauma occurs, the community heals the wounds by each individual detecting its injured neighbors and redirecting resources to those in need, often themselves migrating to the injured area to replace lost cells. All of these healthy functions proceed in a rather reliable manner, despite the complete absence of any hierarchical flow of authority within a community of cells.

Cell communities accomplish these coordinated and cooperative efforts using a powerful tool: sensitivity. The surface of each cell is dotted with receptors, microscopic loading docks that allow foreign molecules to access or influence the interior of the cell. Molecules travel through the intercellular areas, serving as messengers to nearby neighbors. These molecules have diverse characteristics and they include hormones, pheromones, neurotransmitters and nutrients. The cell surface receptors match specifically with these messenger molecules. Many of these molecules influence chemical reactions inside the cell after docking on the surface, changing the function of the cell without ever actually traversing the cell membrane. They initiate signaling cascades which can alter gene expression, energy usage, proliferation rate, and myriad other characteristics and functions of the cell.

In biological contexts, leadership is equivalent to sensitivity. It is by detecting and responding to the individual's local environment that function is directed. Neighbors provide all the guidance that a cell requires in order to promote the health and vitality of its community.

My church leaders, with their teachings about hierarchical social structure, seemed to be convinced that sensitivity, communication and reciprocity would be insufficient means of managing our community. We believed that leaders were essential to our church's health and that a leaderless group would inevitably become directionless, reacting to whim. While the unthinking, unconscious nature of cells certainly eliminates a number of dangers that we encounter in our human interactions, it's notable that our healthy physical bodies are comprised of leaderless communities. Reciprocity and local sensitivity form the foundation of our biological health, and I can only imagine that to rely on these guiding principles more heavily — rather than on hierarchical chains of command — will introduce newfound freedom and equity to our human communities.

At the end of my dad's youth group retreat teaching, the one presented exclusively to young women, he returned to the core of his message. It was the common thread that ran through every teaching at the youth group retreat. "Love," he said, "isn't a feeling. It's not an emotion and it's not butterflies in your stomach. Love is putting the interests of someone else ahead of your own interests."

Our definition of love reflected our fundamentally individualistic view of humanity. We assumed that every person has their own specific interests, their own trajectory, and when these interests would conflict or collide with another person's, we'd need a way to decide whose interests would prevail. In our view, if one person in a relationship would pursue their own interests, the interests of the other would be neglected. If one person would win, the other would lose. This view made sense to me, in light of our adamant and regularly reiterated belief in the total depravity of humanity. This belief prevented us from trusting people to work out conflicts in an egalitarian manner. We believed this would only result in self-serving independence, and to maintain the health of the community, we needed a pre-determined structure for conflict resolution. This is why female submission was so important to us: we believed that conflict was inevitable in relationships, and that a gender-determined hierarchy would allow us to avoid and resolve conflict.

In retrospect, now that I can see the injustice and manipulation involved in this hierarchical gender-based system of power dynamics, I ask myself why I so readily accepted a narrative that presumed my own inferiority. My acceptance of this teaching was based in more than just youth group peer pressure, eagerness to please my respected elders or a genuine belief in God. There was another layer involved, another factor that drew me, oddly enough, toward an unquestioning acceptance of my own subordination. The narrative of hierarchical gender roles told me that I had a place in the Kingdom of God. Though I'd never be a leader, a preacher or the head of my own household, this narrative gave me the comfort of having what I believed to be a God-given place in the world. The notion of self-esteem was mocked in our church, even from the pulpit. Instead, we were told on a regular basis that we—and the rest of humanity—were evil, sinful and depraved, in need of Christ's substitutionary atonement. Against this backdrop, any sense of significance, belonging or goodness felt like an affirmation. I was hungry enough for a sense of meaning in my life that I was willing to accept a narrative declaring my own inherent inferiority. Even if my place was to follow, receive direction and remain quiet in church, at least I had a place.

This sense of meaning and place could only carry me so far, though. It was fundamentally restrictive and confining. I believed that my femininity was a limitation, and that this limitation was God-given. It seemed that God made females because he needed a population to help, follow and support the male leadership in his church. It seemed I was expected to silence and suppress any part of myself that was independent, creative or ambitious.

Aside from my religious upbringing, simply as a millennial American kid, individualism was an important aspect of my understanding of my world. My understanding of personal responsibility was built on the idea that I was a solitary individual, and in order to belong in a community, I needed to contribute to that community. Doing my chores at home was a necessary component of belonging there. Likewise, I was expected to serve in my church and to make a contribution of my own rather than simply attending church. I couldn't claim to belong there unless I contributed in some way. I'd been taught to work hard in school because I'd be able to use my education to contribute to society someday. Even my Brownie girl scout troop's motto was to "leave a place better than we found it," echoing the importance of contribution. It was the noble alternative to selfishness and independence, and it seemed to be the only way that people could cooperate and work toward common goals.

While individualism and personal responsibility are prevalent values in general American culture, my church had a unique understanding of these values. Cooperating with others and contributing to the Kingdom of God were moral imperatives for us. Jesus spoke in parables about the importance of earning our keep, comparing us to branches on a vine, where the non-productive branches are ruthlessly and unhesitatingly cut off and thrown into the fire (John 15:1-11). He was clear about our purpose and responsibility: produce fruit. Contribute. Without a product, we'd be dead weight, and Jesus said we'd no longer belong in the greater whole.

There are valid and important reasons to serve others, cooperate and contribute. Our lifespans and spheres of direct influence are miniscule on a cosmic scale, and we can find a sense of belonging and significance by working toward cooperative goals in our communities. We can find a sense of meaning and purpose in the help we give to others or in what our work produces.

For me though, as a young adult, hopelessness began to settle in my spirit. I realized that I would never be trusted in my church community the way that every man seemed to be unquestioningly trusted. If my thoughts would ever be heard by my church leaders, they'd be first funneled through a male who had authority over me. As a young single woman, I felt a sense of dread at the thought of being expected to spend my life obeying and submitting to a husband's plans, goals and ideas. I was expected to silence a part of my personality, for no reason other than my femininity, and I was told that I would find fulfillment while functioning as a truncated form of myself. The pain of being led to embrace these arbitrary limitations on my behavior and interactions rapidly eclipsed the sense of purpose that my conviction afforded me.

As so often was the case in my evangelical culture, as soon as we found an ideology that we could support with biblical passages, and that made some sense or had some benefit, we stopped turning the kaleidoscope. Any re-evaluation of hierarchical gender roles was met with strong resistance and instead the teaching that these roles are distinct—despite cultural movements to expand traditional gender roles—was ardently propagated. We persistently held the kaleidoscope steady, fixed on this one image, emphatically insisting that this was the only valid way of seeing things.

My church community had a reason to value productivity and cooperation that was completely unrelated to gender. We read the parable of the vine and branches as a warning of the judgment that we would receive if we failed to remain productive, contributing members of our communities. The fate of the unproductive branch—being cut off and cast into the fire—sounded so similar to eternal damnation and punishment in the flames of hell that we believed it couldn't be merely coincidental. In a community that mocked the notion of self-esteem and regularly reiterated a belief in total human depravity, productivity seemed to be a path toward validating my existence. I believed my worth would be determined by means of transactions.

It didn't take long, however, for this thought pattern to create incredible anxiety.

Am I making the right kind of contribution—am I producing the right kind of fruit?

How do I know when I've produced enough fruit to earn my place?

Do I just have to keep up with the people around me, or am I being judged on the basis of some universal standard?

I believed my sole purpose was to contribute, as it seemed God would not hesitate to discard me if I became unproductive. I found myself in a continuously looping spiral of shame, comparing my product—my contribution—with that of others. Whether in friendships, in my family, in school or in church, the comparison-obsession was pervasive and insidious. No matter how much I accomplished, what I produced or how I contributed, I could always imagine that I could have done more. The ensuing self-disgust and self-hatred became deeply familiar to me, always haunting my thoughts.

The toxicity of linking personal value with personal contribution was not solely psychological and personal, but it damaged my relationships too. My misguided attempt to build healthy relationships by minimizing my own needs began to backfire, leading me to become more and more resentful and critical. The more I tried to ignore my own needs—to minimize myself—and resolved to always give and never take, the more I resented those who didn't seem to be matching my level of sacrifice. I became an expert at identifying non-contributors: those who take more than they give, who eat up others' time and resources without giving in return. I kept mental rankings of the people I knew, based on contributions they made and the product they produced. Although I tried to keep these mental scoring systems private, they leaked out, and even if I didn't explicitly state them, I have no doubt I expressed them in my treatment of others. My beliefs created a judgmental mindset that undoubtedly colored my treatment of those around me.

No matter how much I accomplished, I still wondered if God saw me as lazy. No matter how much I tried to serve at church services and youth group events, I still wondered if I was contributing enough. No matter how much I tried to minimize my opinions and thoughts, submitting to the male leadership around me, I worried that I was becoming an overbearing woman, rejecting what I'd been taught was my biblical feminine role. The Kingdom of God was turning out to be a system in which it was impossible not to be disappointed with myself.

Jesus used the parable of the vine and branches to communicate how important it is to be productive and to contribute in the Kingdom of God. This parable was directly inspired by the natural world; from plant biology in particular, and I can't help but notice that this was a common practice of his. He often used examples from nature to make his point. The lilies of the field, the principle of sowing and reaping, the vine and branches and the barren fig tree all served as metaphors or examples in the teachings of Jesus. Maybe he made this choice because of the prevalence of agriculture in his audience's society. Maybe it was the enduring nature of these principles that made these natural examples especially powerful, allowing us to still understand them today. I do have to wonder, though if there was a further reason that Jesus made this choice. Nature seems to reflect universal principles; there's something inherent in biology that gives us a clue about how all of life—even our human experience—works.

Aside from biblical use of biological metaphors, I've always had a particular type of admiration for biological systems. While I, with my self-interested human nature, had to be taught how to work with others and contribute to something greater than myself, biological systems do so naturally. Biological systems are some of the most efficiently structured, well-organized communities we can find on the planet. Even the vocabulary we use to describe biological systems evokes images of machines, painting a picture of order, structure and productivity. Biology textbooks describe cells as factories, and enzymes as workers on a factory floor, efficiently producing proteins from the resources available to them and the recipes found in their genes.

Cell components work around the clock, transcribing and translating DNA strands in precise choreography. These processes that occur on the interiors of cells are optimally coordinated in order to conserve as much energy and as many resources as possible, producing protein products while requiring minimal input. The cooperation and coordination in a cell are undeniable. It's a world where each small part makes its own distinct and specialized contribution to the whole. Every part of a cell fulfills a specific and essential role in sustaining the productivity of the factory.

A pristine example of the coordination, choreography and organization within our cells is the continuously looping process known as the cell cycle. It's a series of phases, each occurring after another in a predictable progression, culminating in proliferation. A cell's activities can be categorized according to its current phase in the cell cycle. The cell cycle is not perpetual though, because of course, cells do not live forever. Human skin cells, for instance only live for about a month, and before they die, they must make their own replacements. If they fail to make replacements, the body won't be able to keep surviving after they die. Our cells have a contribution to make.

There's a succession of intricately detailed steps that must occur correctly at each stage of proliferation, which together produce daughter cells that each contain exactly one copy of DNA, properly formed organelles, exactly one precisely organized nucleus and just the right amount of cytoplasm. If any significant parameter is incorrect, failing to match the prototype, the cell won't survive. Or worse, the cell will survive and will malfunction, damaging the entire body. Proper cell productivity relies on precise adherence to appropriate cell cycle progression.

It seems that if a cell stops participating in the proliferation cycle, it would just be dead weight. It would be like a branch that doesn't bear fruit. Just as we'd expect from any efficient, productive machine, cells have a mechanism for removing dead weight from the body. Malfunctioning cells are targeted for apoptosis, which is a self-initiated pathway toward cell death. It's a tightly controlled, elaborately choreographed process that specifically targets and kills a cell. It's the original sniper operation, but it's not an attack from an outsider. It originates within the organism itself. Apoptosis seems to be one more biological metaphor for God's plan for people who are lazy and unproductive: "every branch...that does not bear fruit I will take away."

There is, however, a phase of the cell cycle that is left out of this picture. In biology textbook cell cycle diagrams, a tiny exit ramp is usually drawn off the main circle, heading toward "G0." It's usually just a tiny arrow, and at most it's given only a few sentences of explanation in an introductory text. G0 is called quiescence, a state of dormancy. Cells in G0 do not produce replacement daughter cells. G0 cells slow down, stop growing and lie dormant. G0 is only a temporary state of dormancy; these cells can be reawakened at any time. Quiescence is not a pathway toward death, but instead these cells are simply resting. G0 cells stay alive, continuing to consume resources and take up space in the body, but failing to give or produce anything in return. Quiescent cells don't seem to fit into the model of efficient machine-like productivity that I learned to apply to biological systems. How could an efficient machine allow these selfish consumers to keep taking up space?

Quiescent cells were not investigated in detail until decades after they were discovered. This cell cycle phase was initially thought to be an emergency response. Quiescent cells, while they continue to consume nutrients and resources, require less than normally proliferating cells require. Because of this, it seemed reasonable to assume quiescence to be a survival mechanism, employed when nutrients and growth areas are limited. Alternatively, G0 was thought to be a defective state, in which apoptosis has failed to properly initiate, the pathway that would remove the non-contributors. Neither of these explanations of quiescence warranted further investigation into this phase of cell life, so for years, research funds and efforts were directed toward the cell populations that seemed to be more relevant to life and health: proliferating cells. This was certainly a reasonable prioritization, given the number of research questions surrounding normal cells that remain unanswered, even today.

In the late 1980s and early 1990s, however, quiescent cells caught the attention of the biological research community. Tools had been developed to test a population of cells and determine if they were quiescent, facilitating further investigation into G0 phase. Contrary to the presumption that G0 is a rare state of dormancy that only occurs in extreme conditions, these investigations revealed that the vast majority of cells in an adult human body are quiescent at any given time. G0 was found to be the most common cellular state (Daignan-Fornier 2011). It could no longer be considered an aberration; it was now clear that quiescence is the most normal state a human cell can occupy. The recognition of its prevalence brought cellular dormancy into focus for biological researchers.

This overwhelming prevalence made it difficult to explain quiescence simply as a survival mechanism. It became clear that it was implausible to conclude that these cells were all actively responding to emergencies at all times, and it seemed unlikely that a state this common would serve no purpose of its own within the organism. These cells had to be making some contribution to their community. There had to be some reason for the body to continue maintaining them.

One technique that is used for assessing basic cellular characteristics is gene expression profiling. Every cell contains a DNA molecule, a coil of double helical strands. The DNA molecule is located deep at the cell's core, wound tightly around protein spools and kept in the rounded double-membrane-encased organelle known as the nucleus. The DNA molecule within every cell in one person's body is an identical copy of the DNA molecule in every other cell within that person's body. DNA gives each person their distinct identity, so it's crucial that all copies be exactly the same. This means that your liver cells have the same DNA molecule as your skin cells, your kidney cells, your heart cells and your pancreatic cells. And yet, each one of these cell types has distinct characteristics, performs distinct functions and produces different protein profiles, even though they all start with the same set of genetic instructions.

Epigenetics explains how this is possible. While every cell in a person's body contains an identical copy of DNA, not every gene within that DNA molecule is active in every cell. The modulating, fine-tuning power of epigenetic factors — our cells' complex, sensitive and multifaceted system of genetic dimmer switches — controls which genetic regions are producing proteins in a given cell at a given time. Not only is gene expression cell type-specific, but throughout the lifetime of a cell, its gene expression profile changes in a cell cycle-dependent fashion. Each phase of the cellular life cycle is characterized by changes to the cell's gene expression profile. Assessing a cell population's expression profile has become a common initial step toward identifying general characteristics of that cell population.

When the expression profile of quiescent cell populations was first determined, a group of genes that had never before been associated with each other was identified in high abundance (Schneider 1988; Coppock 1993). When the protein products of these genes were specifically targeted and their expression suppressed, the cells exited G0 phase and re-entered the cell proliferation cycle. The protein products expressed by this unique set of genes, never before linked with one another, are responsible for keeping quiescent cells in this state of dormancy. The abundance of this unique set of proteins suggests that quiescence is an actively maintained state. After this discovery was made, quiescence could no longer be considered to be a defective state. The cell biology world now knew quiescence to be an actively supported state (Coller 2006). In other words, it was now clear that the non-contributor is specifically supported as a member of the body.

After screening cell populations for quiescence, researchers found that organisms with shorter lifespans generally contain lower percentages of quiescent cells than organisms with longer lifespans. Over a relatively short span of time, quiescent cells make no obvious contribution, but over a longer timeframe, and within the context of the entire organism, these dormant populations play critical roles. Without support from quiescent populations, maximum human lifespans would be several decades shorter. Reserves of dormant cells allow for humans to continue to live long after reaching full body size, for the duration of adulthood. The non-contributor plays an essential role after all.

As a pre-teen listening to youth group retreat teachings, I believed there were only two mutually exclusive communal alternatives: independent, self-serving individuality or hierarchical cooperation. Our biology illustrates a third possibility: reciprocity. Our bodies are cooperating communities of cells with no single designated leader. Each organ and system functions in coordination with the others, and during phases when one individual is dormant, the others pick up the slack. Each part has a function, and these functions adapt and evolve over the course of life. Sometimes the function of one component is simply dormancy.

Biological systems do not require their members to earn their keep, and they have no requirements for output or contribution. Our bodies function on the basis of mutual support and generous reciprocity.

In the cellular realm, participation is more important than contribution. Even those parts of the whole that seem to be serving no purpose are actually performing an essential role. They appear to be taking up space without making a productive contribution, but in reality, they're essential participants in the greater whole. A quiescent cell *does* bear fruit, to use the language of John 15. Its fruit can't be measured or quantified in the moment, but over time, its effects will be fully seen.

Our biological nature is characterized by relentless inclusion and rich diversity. Not only do distinct parts serve distinct functions, but the purpose of some parts may be to serve no directly observable function. There are pieces of the whole whose roles are to lie dormant. They look like dead weight. They look like non-contributors. But over a longer timescale, they are essential participants. This dormant, unproductive temporary dead weight will allow the system to persist much longer than it otherwise could.

What if I apply this new definition of "contributing" to the way I conduct my life? When I recognize that participation, rather than production, is my purpose, my self-scrutiny starts to dissipate. I become less critical and judgmental toward others. I realize that my contributions come in many forms, and these contributions cannot be directly compared with those of others. I start to see the value of those parts of my own personality that seem to slow me down. I can begin to pay attention to my tendencies that block my own productivity, and I can look for the ways in which these tendencies actually help me. Sometimes these tendencies slow me down enough to reconsider and re-evaluate my activities. Sometimes they allow me to heighten my sensitivity toward others in my community.

This assumption of the value of participation, rather than contribution, strengthens my patience with the changing of my own life phases. There are times when I will provide a measurable contribution or service to my society, and there will also be times when my contribution is not readily observable. My role in my community, my personal dignity and my value do not rely on my observable contribution. What drives me in this context, what anchors me to my community is not the fruit I bear but instead is my persistent will to participate in the greater whole.

When I realize that my relationships are not simply based on the contribution I could make to another, but on my readiness to participate with another, I open myself to engage in reciprocity. I find ways to be assertive while still being respectful. Love becomes a flow rather than an exchange; a state rather than a transaction.

Nature teaches me radical inclusiveness. Biology suggests that my belonging is inherent in my existence, and that each of us, at each stage of life, can claim this as the basis for our dignity and belonging. My contribution does not validate my existence, but my existence itself — the fact that I am participating in the greater whole — secures my place within that whole. To extend this radically inclusive generosity to myself and my neighbors requires patience and hope. I need patience to continue to validate myself when my work provides no immediately observable product. I need hope to believe it is worthwhile to engage in reciprocal, mutual love without tallying and score-keeping.

Reciprocity allows us to leave transactional forms of love behind. Love is deeper and more constant than that. There will be seasons of dormancy for me as there will be for each of us, seasons when I seem to have no purpose or function and when I can't use my contributions to justify my belonging. In these moments, my path to freedom is to recognize that the contribution I once made was never the key to my validation in the first place. I've belonged here all along, and I've never had to prove it. Radical inclusion is the story imprinted in nature, from my biology to my human experience.

5

IDENTITY IN CHRIST

The final moment was always the worst. It was that last heartbeat right before the casket would open, when everything seemed to stand still. My instincts commanded me to hold my breath but I fought the urge and kept my breathing steady, shallow and imperceptible. I was no rookie. I knew better than to show the audience any signs that I was breathing. I was, after all, playing the role of "corpse."

Twenty seconds earlier, the audience had shuffled into the room, and all they knew was that this was a pitch-black space, their first indoor stop on the haunted house tour. Outside, they had stopped first to watch a fake teenage drunk driving car accident. The audience watched as five teenagers limped out of two mangled cars and realized that their friend had died. Her lifeless body was sprawled across the hood of the car, a piece of windshield still protruding from the prosthetic wound on her neck, and more shards of shattered glass surrounding her body. The survivors of the car crash mourned their friend with screams and desperate pleas with God, all against a backdrop of angry death metal. The tour guide, a scythe-bearing grim reaper would then lead the audience to the second stop in the haunted house tour. They went to the deceased teenager's gravesite to watch as her mother and little sister grieved. The stories the sobbing mother told about her daughter's short life were, of course, fabricated, often improvised, but her anger and frustration seemed genuine. She embodied a desperation that is familiar to anyone who has experienced loss, and the audience members often had tears in their eyes as they watched this heartbroken mother mourn her child's untimely death.

Now, at the third stop of their tour, the audience was indoors. The tension was higher in here. Outside, they'd at least had the comfort of the parking lot lights, the moon and the few stars visible on an overcast October night in the suburbs of Pittsburgh. Here, they had no such comfort and no clue about what would come next.

From my place inside the coffin, I could hear muffled whispers and timid shuffles as the audience members made hesitant movements. Every once in a while, a sharp 'yelp' rose up from the huddled crowd. The startled reactions made me smile, lying on my back in the dark inside the coffin. Those sounds of shock were good signs. This was not just a haunted house, this was an evangelistic Christian haunted house, and any indication of fear, shock or sadness was a sure sign that conversions would soon follow.

The lid of my coffin blocked out the light, so a wave of gasps and a few startled shrieks were my signal that the lights had come on.

"OPEN THE BOX."

It was my dad's voice, in its most commanding and clear tone. I heard the lid scrape off the wooden coffin and a puff of fake-smoke-filled air brushed my face and neck and my folded hands, limply draped across my stomach. My gently closed eyelids filtered the bright lights, flooding my eyes with a pink hue. I exerted every bit of effort to keep my eyelids completely still and my breathing imperceptible.

"ARISE." That was my cue. I took a deep, exaggerated

breath, dramatically coughing, choking and hiccupping as I revived. My coffin was lying on the ground in front of the judgment throne of God. After a few dramatic blinks and staggered breaths, I sat up in the coffin. There, elevated on a 20-foot platform in front of a wall covered in reflective Mylar, was my father. He was dressed in sparkling white and silver robes, his face, neck and hands covered in a thick layer of glittery white makeup, with a bejeweled costume store crown sitting on top of his head. My church's haunted house budget was small, but our dedication made up for our limited resources. Sitting inside the coffin, staring up at him with wide eyes, I didn't even notice how over-the-top his costume was. I only saw his stern, unblinking eyes.

We began our usual exchange of dialogue. We performed this scene 40+ times every show night, so it was well-memorized at this point. He told me that my name was not written in the Book of Life and I began to plead with him to spare me from hell. My pleading began with confusion and shock, then grew into exasperation, and finally reached a fever pitch of hysterical desperation. At no point in my pleading, however, was I talking nonsense. I had a central argument, and it was that I'd done the best I could. I made slight changes to the specific points of my argument with each performance, but the theme stayed the same:

"I went to church EVERY Sunday!"

"I gave money to charity!"

"I volunteered in my neighborhood!"

"I never lied!"

I always ended my pleas with my signature move: pivoting to face the crowd while turning my back to the judgment throne of God. I would anxiously scan the faces I saw in the audience until I found someone with the wide eyes and furrowed brow that signaled my performance was provoking the desired response. I stretched out my arm as far as possible, pointing directly at the furrowed brow and locking eyes with the stranger, boring into them with a deranged look of hysteria. "God, I was JUST LIKE HIM!"

My glitter-enshrouded dad looked up from his podium, locking eyes with me: "Depart from me; I never knew you!" He turned in one swift motion, hiding his face from me as he slammed the Book of Life shut. It was just a dictionary covered in glittery white paper, but the sharp *crack!* convinced everyone in the room that the decision was serious and final. The bright lights cut out at the same instant the book closed. Strobe lights came on, aggressively grating death metal exploded through a set of floor speakers surrounding the audience, and three of my friends from youth group, dressed in all black, hooded, caped and masked, rushed out of a corner closet and dragged me off to eternal torture. They let go of me once we were out of the audience's view, releasing me into a closet that was about two feet by three feet. I continued on, shuffling through a makeshift passageway and emerging at my next performance location in the evangelistic haunted house: hell.

My futile pleas with God at the judgment throne were based on my actions — my behavior, my choices, the way I lived. In our church, behavior was a key component of our Christian lives, an outward sign of our commitment to godliness. We believed God had standards pertaining to the way we would eat, sleep, work, manage money, entertain ourselves and relate to one another. But the haunted house taught me that none of this would ultimately matter. None of my behaviors and actions would prevent me from going to hell. At the judgment throne, God would be interested in something deeper than behaviors. God would judge me on the basis of who I was at my core. He could see right through my actions and he could tell when I was just performing empty gestures. God would judge me on the basis of my identity.

After being left in that back closet, I stood for a moment, my hand on my hip, breathing heavily as I recovered from sixty seconds of desperately flailing, screaming and struggling against the hooded and caped demons who were dragging me off to hell. My friend's dad was sitting on a stool behind a sound control board, working under the light of a single red lightbulb. Both of his thumbs were raised up to shoulder level, his eyebrows furrowed to let me know his adulation was genuine, and he was slowly shaking his head back and forth. Without making a sound, he mouthed "Wow, amazing, Beth!"

I beamed a wide smile, letting him know how much his affirmation meant to me without making a sound. I wanted so badly to deliver a convincing performance. Eternal salvations were depending on my ability to portray anguish and despair.

The audience was undoubtedly experiencing a blend of fright, horror and entertainment at this point, as they were being shuffled along, listening to a short monologue from their grim reaper tour guide before eventually arriving in hell. He explained the inevitability of damnation for all who do not believe in their hearts that Jesus is Lord.

Once they turned the final corner of the hallway into hell, the audience would see me there along with a few dozen other tortured souls chained to the walls or trapped in cages along the floor. They'd see Satan there, elevated up on the stage, and they'd know it was Satan because of his red body paint, his plastic pitchfork, purchased from a Halloween costume store and the rubber horns glued onto his red skullcap.

Handcuffed and chained to that stage next to Satan, I was acting, of course, simply pretending to be tortured, but there was something that felt real about playing this role night after night. With each performance, I revisited the pain of rejection and the horror of realizing my insufficiency once it was simply too late. The slamming of the Book of Life, the dropping of the curtain and the separation from God felt real to me, and with repetition, the sense of abandonment and rejection became more and more visceral. Hell was supposed to be the apex of the haunted house's horror, but for me, by the time I arrived in hell, the terror had already peaked. The worst had already happened. God had rejected me.

My fellow actors, most of them members of my church, were eager to congratulate me at the end of each performance night. Between performances, the volunteer makeup artists, sound technicians and errand runners would all make a point of encouraging me, telling me how it blessed them to see me using my gifts for the Kingdom of God. "You're such a good actress!" they said. "You really make it seem real!" No one ever seemed to notice that my fear actually *was* real. It wasn't an act. I actually believed the message of the haunted house: that my own judgment day would arrive when I'd die, and on that day, my eternal fate would be sealed.

The final stop along the haunted house tour was a counseling room. Here, every visitor was told how to avoid eternal damnation by following instructions we lifted directly from a literal interpretation of Romans 10:9. "If you confess with your mouth that Jesus is Lord and believe in your heart that God raised him from the dead, you will be saved." We kept track of the number of visitors each night who chose to "accept Jesus into their hearts," and at our cast debriefing after each night's series of performances, we'd celebrate our evangelistic victories. We prayed all year long that souls would be saved and lives would be changed at this haunted house, and we believed that each person who chose to believe in Jesus after those performances was a direct answer to our prayers.

Although we rejoiced and celebrated these responses to the haunted house, the haunted house wasn't only for the newly saved converts. It was for us too. We wanted to remind ourselves about hell; to remind ourselves why it was important to serve God, trust Jesus and avoid sin. For me, it worked. At the end of each performance night that I spent being repeatedly rejected and abandoned by God and tortured by Satan, I was deeply and thoroughly reminded of hell. These performance nights transformed my fear of God's rejection into a palpable, panicky terror.

I was alone in the coffin every night. When I would plead with God at the judgment throne, virtue by comparison meant nothing. God didn't care about how I measured up against all the other youth group kids. He never cared about the way I simply acted or appeared. My good deeds and my seemingly godly outward behavior couldn't cover over the evil that was at my core. God judged me on the basis of my individual, isolated identity. The final words were the same every night: "Depart from me, for I never knew you." The message I received from this portrayal of God was that I had a true identity, buried beneath the artificial one that I showed to everyone around me, and at the end of my life, this true identity would be all that would matter.

I was in the midst of my adolescence when I performed as a coffin girl, a particularly impressionable phase of life when I was trying to figure out how the world works. The things I experienced, saw and heard during my teen years imprinted themselves especially deeply. The haunted house was an especially extreme case of this deep imprinting. Like muscle memory, the coffin-girl experience lingered, sometimes manifesting as a visceral nightmarish terror and other times simply as a lurking suspicion that I, at my deepest, truest core, was not good enough, holy enough, pure enough, or obedient enough to make it onto God's list of redeemable souls.

I tried my best to channel my fear into action and I became a really good evangelical kid. When I chose my college, I made sure to find a nearby evangelical non-denominational church. I humbly bragged to my friends that I was choosing to attend a public university so that I would be able to be a light to the world, evangelizing the students I'd meet on my secular campus, but I would still develop my faith at church.

The church had a college ministry group that met on campus in the student union building every Tuesday night. The interior walls of the meeting room were made entirely of windows, so everyone who walked by would see our raised hands and our passionate expressions during our acoustic sing-alongs and prayer circles. I always arrived early to "serve." I'd help to set up the sound equipment, or organize the chairs in tidy rows. In my mind, serving my church community was a way I showed that my inner transformation was real. "It's important to show outward expression of inward transformation," we would say. We prayed for inner transformation and we worked hard to demonstrate it outwardly. Looking back now, I imagine my freshman roommate must have thought I was simply chasing the social image of a respectable Christian kid, trying to convince my Christian friends of my own virtue. She didn't know that I alone was the one I was trying to convince, desperate to prove to myself that my faith was real. The busier I made myself by doing the "work of the Kingdom," the less I feared that what I called belief was simply wishful thinking.

Each meeting started with a time of worship. I'd learned the routine by now, and my gestures, facial expressions and tones of voice had become incorporated into my churchgoer muscle memory. I stood at my seat, taking my place in my row of college ministry students, all of us facing the acoustic guitarist in the front. I followed along, singing the words that were projected onto the screen behind him, squinting my eyes closed, lifting my hands and contorting my face into a passionate grimace to indicate my devotion and earnestness. I always kept my eyes open just enough to let in a slit of light. I never wanted anyone to know I was watching, but I scanned the faces in the room.

And the cry of my heart
Is to bring You praise
From the inside out
Lord my soul cries out

All of the other faces in the room had earnestness written all over them. Everyone else seemed to really mean it. I wanted to mean it. More than anything, I wanted to mean it. At least once a day my mind would flash back to the image of the judgment throne of God, the slammed-shut Book of Life and the demons dragging me off to eternal torture. I might be able to fool my church friends and even my parents, but I believed God would see through my facade of belief. God knew that my words were aspirational at best, and that praising him was not actually the "cry of my heart." I knew how small of a portion of each day I actually spent thinking about God or praying, and singing these words at college ministry just felt fraudulent.

The guitarist ended the song and began a prayer. His eyes were squeezed shut and his brow furrowed deeply. His words were breathy, low in tone and passionate. "God, help us find our identity in you. Help us to set aside anything on earth that falsely claims to give us our identity and help us to serve you wholly." We believed God wanted to be our one and only source of identity, and that any meaning and purpose we found elsewhere would ultimately take away from our identity in Christ.

This phrase — "identity in Christ" — was one I'd heard a lot by the time I was in college. When I talked about my identity, I was talking about my meaning, purpose, and grounding in life. I was talking about my central, defining elements. My identity was the collection of factors making me distinct from anyone else. As a Christian, I believed I should carefully select where I chose to find my identity. I believed that the story of Christ's crucifixion and resurrection gave meaning to my life. Part of this meaning was sharing the gospel with others and part of this meaning was simply living in communion with God. As an evangelical Christian, I intentionally tried to find my identity in God rather than in any aspect of my earthly life. I was aiming for steadfastness, and I believed that the only firm foundation was Christ. This identity, I believed, would stay the same throughout my life, regardless of the changes that would occur in my circumstances and surroundings.

"Finding my identity in Christ" had a clear meaning for me. It meant that achievements, interests, money, relationships and social standing would not define me. My belief that I was chosen, redeemed and set apart from the rest of the world would define me. I believed that any other source of identity would simply compete with my identity in Christ. If I allowed temporary earthly sources of identity to define me — money, achievements, roles and even relationships — these would detract from my identity as one of God's people, redeemed from sin by Christ and set apart from the rest of the world.

For me, college ministry was a pursuit of my identity in Christ. The haunted house had taught me that my actions would not be enough to ensure that I'd be accepted by God. I longed to experience the type of transformation that would place my name in the Book of Life. I kept turning my fear into action. I showed up each week at college ministry, ready to engage in the mental calisthenics required to try and stop thinking about anything other than God. I tried my best to empty my brain of my typical freshman thoughts. I wasn't supposed to be thinking about the cute boy who caught my eye, the homework I had to do later that night, the exam coming up next week or the way my roommate snapped at me the other night. Any thought that wasn't about God, I believed, would usurp God. I thought there were two mutually exclusive categories for my attention: God and everything else. In order to find my identity in Christ, I earnestly tried to minimize everything else.

Of course, I only succeeded in singularly focusing on God for about 15 seconds at a time. I never quite knew how to stay focused on the things I sang about: God's holiness, God's goodness or God's grace. None of these ideas felt all that accessible to me. I didn't really know what any of this meant and it never took long before I'd get bored of thinking about God. I spent most of my time at college ministry cycling in and out of anxiety and fear that my wandering thoughts revealed the phoniness of my faith. I wasn't just afraid that my worldly thoughts would be revealed to my Christian friends—I could handle that. I was terrified that my phoniness would be revealed before the judgment throne of God himself.

I un-furrowed my brow and opened my eyes fully, studying the worship leader's face. Was it just the stage, the microphone and acoustic guitar that made him look so earnest? If I could ask him one-on-one, would he admit that these words he was singing so passionately were only really true for a fraction of his day? I studied his face, fruitlessly searching for a sign of self-doubt. Everyone except me seemed authentically engaged.

After worship, we divided ourselves into small discussion groups, and we shared personal ways in which we were grateful to God. We had a short list of questions to discuss, all guiding us toward specific real-life examples of what we believed to be God's grace in our lives. I listened as my fellow students shared anecdotes that indicated how faithful, loving and kind God had been toward them. I heard the various familiar phrases that all indicated the same general information: "evidence of God's grace," "unmerited favor," or "God at work in my life." It seemed they had some type of assurance that I simply didn't have. It sounded like they had actually been transformed from the inside out, and I was the only one faking it, desperately grasping for belief and trying to make it genuine. My belief was always vanishing, disappearing just moments after I resolved to make God most important in my life. I had a comfortable, peaceful life but even so, my daily concerns were constantly vying for my attention, usurping the place that I believed should belong to Christ. My world just wasn't simple enough for the simplicity of this gospel message. My eternal destiny was, however, at stake and it depended on my confidence in my own faith. This is what kept me searching for my own identity in Christ.

I never dared to be honest about this at college ministry meetings, but I had no choice other than to be honest with myself. In my quiet moments, I was terrified. I could perform well enough to convince the college ministry group that my faith was genuine, but God couldn't be fooled. Everyone else seemed so sure that they knew God, that they loved God, and that God was faithful. I could sing about my blessed assurance; I could close my eyes, furrow my brow and use the passionate vocal inflection that would convince everyone in the room that I believed. But God would know I didn't.

I believed that if I could find my identity in Christ, the Christian life would come naturally to me. My godliness would be undeniable and everything I would do would flow from this foundation. My identity in Christ would naturally produce Christlike behavior. I wouldn't have to wonder whether or not I was a strong enough believer or if I was committed enough to my faith. I would no longer wonder whether or not I was a true Christian, and I wouldn't have to muster up my faith or force my godly behavior. It would be as natural as the beating of my heart or the inflation of my lungs. Christ would define me and distinguish me, as long as I was faithful to build my identity on the foundation of his truth.

My identity includes so much more than this. There's an aspect of my individual identity that is tangible, concrete and visible, unlike the often-elusive internal identity I sought to find in Christ when I was a college student. I have a physical identity. Somehow, wondrously and inexplicably, every cell in my body is marked with my identity. Each cell contains the specific information and machinery necessary to be a part of me. The molecular explanation for my physical identity — the specificity and constancy of my genetic code — doesn't eliminate the sense of mystery and wonder I feel when I think about the physical manifestation of individual identity. The cells in my body exhibit wild diversity in their specialized expression of my genetic code, but also tightly organized coordination in their careful maintenance of this singular code. I find it remarkable, and even baffling that this system functions with such resilience and robustness.

Despite the constant turnover of cells — the process of cellular aging, death and replacement — I continue being myself. As a young student of science, the explanation of this phenomenon seemed simple. I have a unique DNA code, as does every person, and one copy of this code is found in every cell of my body, spooled into an elaborately well-organized coil. This DNA code distinguishes me from others, defines and predicts my physical characteristics, my propensity toward various diseases and even my mental state. This code is unique to me, having been determined at the instant my father's sperm and my mother's egg fused to create a single-celled organism. This code, determined once and for all at this earliest moment of my own life, forms the foundation of my individual identity. It's essential that this code stay the same throughout my entire life. This code is astonishingly versatile, supporting my development from single-celled organism to embryo to fetus to viable infant to adult. Throughout all of this physical transformation, though, my genes remain steadfast. Only in the event of a defect, or the introduction of disease-causing damage, do we expect a genetic code to change.

As an evangelical undergraduate, biology gave me the perfect metaphor by which to illustrate my quest to find my identity in Christ. My pursuit of an unshakeable, clearly definable core identity — the kind that would be as concrete and identifiable as the DNA molecule in my cells — was the reason I spent my free time at college ministry meetings every Tuesday night and church every Sunday, and the reason I wanted to have friendships with other Christian students. I wanted Christ to be the code that dictated who I was. I wanted to make it undeniable and permanent that Christ was my identity. I was trying to prove to myself that I had been born again, that I'd found a new identity, and that I was now one of God's set-apart, chosen and redeemed children.

Understandably, it is a priority within human cells to protect and maintain DNA molecules. These double-helical DNA strands are too important, too foundational and too fundamental for health for the body to take any chances with their molecular structure. Complex systems of DNA protection and maintenance are in effect within human cells. This precious molecule is never left vulnerably out in the open, but is stored deep inside the cell's core, in the nucleus, wrapped tightly around protein spools called histones. It can only be unwound when the cellular community cooperates to unwind it. This cooperative effort initiates in times when the DNA molecule is needed for some purpose; otherwise, the molecule is kept safely spooled inside the nucleus. The coordinated nature of the unspooling ensures that it doesn't initiate erroneously. Even one of the necessary proteins failing to bind where it's supposed to bind, failing to release its interaction with its substrate at the rate it's supposed to do so, or failing to obtain the required ATP-derived energy when it's supposed to could be enough to derail the entire process.

This precise protection of the essential, precious, fundamental DNA is a part of normal, healthy operation for all types of DNA—human, animal, plant, and even bacteria. Bacterial cells, which are complete organisms contained within single cells, follow many of the same patterns that human cells follow, but bacteria are drastically simplified organisms, in comparison with humans. Bacterial cells have much shorter lifetimes than do the cells in our human bodies, so they are much easier to study. The effects of human cell behaviors on the fate of the human body may not become apparent for years, or even decades. When studying bacteria, however, we can understand the organismal effects of cell behaviors much more rapidly. We don't have to wait years in order to see the effect of a change in cell behavior on a bacterial population; the effects become evident within days. In order to understand an aspect of animal, plant or human biology, it's usually helpful to first investigate that aspect within bacterial biology.

As biological investigation of bacteria has progressed, biologists have made a striking number of groundbreaking discoveries. One of these was the discovery of antibiotics. Antibiotics are chemicals that either kill bacteria or slow down their rate of growth. They are effective tools for eliminating bacterial populations in a targeted manner, and they're useful for treating human medical conditions that are caused or propagated by bacterial infections.

While studying antibiotics, biologists began to observe that over time, increasingly higher dosages of antibiotics were necessary in order to kill a bacterial population. The bacteria were gradually developing a tolerance to the antibiotics, and they were doing so by using an incredibly clever tactic: they began learning the mechanisms of bacterial attacks and developing ways to dodge the attacks. They became impervious to the antibiotics, continuing to grow and thrive even though they were in the presence of toxins that were attacking them in customized, targeted ways.

This ability of bacteria to dodge the effects of antibiotics is an amazing example of adaptation. It's a sophisticated survival mechanism. There's an additional aspect of bacterial antibiotic resistance, however, that is not just incredible and sophisticated, it seems impossible. The impossible aspect is the speed with which this resistance develops and spreads. Bacterial resistance is conferred genetically. In the development of bacterial antibiotic resistance, changes are made to the actual genetic code of the bacterial cells, but these changes spread from cell to cell in a much shorter span of time than the time it takes for a generation to pass. Not only this, but resistance continues to spread among bacterial cells even after the antibiotic is removed from contact with the bacterial cells. Somehow the cells respond to a stimulus they never directly received.

The explanation of this phenomenon—the very key to understanding the transmittance of bacterial antibiotic resistance—revolutionized the modern understanding of genetics, inheritance and the attainment of genes. The precise mechanism of the spread of antibiotic resistance puzzled biologists until genetic lab techniques were improved to the point where they could track the spread of the genetic markers of antibiotic resistance. It turns out that the gene for antibiotic resistance is transferred between bacterial cells on the basis of nothing but proximity, as if it is a contagion (Ochman 2000; Keeling 2008). Once the gene is passed from one cell to another, it becomes incorporated into the genome of the acceptor cell, and it functions exactly as though it was a naturally inherited gene. It becomes just as much a part of the identity of the cell as any other gene.

It took time, but this means of acquiring genes, called Horizontal Gene Transfer (HGT), was later observed in all kinds of cells, to include human cells (Dunning Hotopp, 2011; Lacroix 2016). Our most concrete form of physical identity is not so constant after all. It's actually porous and malleable, always shifting, expanding, contracting, and merging with our surroundings. Cells crowd-source their own identities. Our cells don't just exist within their environments; they exist in equilibrium with their environments, being transformed by their surroundings.

My assumption that I had a distinct, unchanging individual identity seemed so commonplace that it was a difficult assumption for me to identify, let alone to question. Cell biology suggests an alternative to this assumption, however. Biology paints a new picture of identity, contradicting what I've always assumed to be true. Especially as a young evangelical, I believed that once I found my identity in Christ, it would be permanent and unshakeable. Biology shows that even the most concrete and seemingly constant type of identity — genetic identity — is constantly transforming.

As a college student searching for my own identity in Christ, I believed that a necessary step would be to disavow all other sources of identity, meaning or purpose; that all other sources of meaning would usurp my godly identity. My cells, however, welcome every available source of identity. From a cell's point of view, it's hard to tell the difference between the environment and the self. Exterior factors define the individual, and it becomes difficult to speak at all of personal identity. My individual separateness seems to be more and more illusory, and it becomes less and less clear where I end and my neighbor begins.

This image of identity is unsettling. My biological form of identity lacks the agency and autonomy that I assume I have as a human. My cells are at the mercy of their environments, absorbing their surroundings and adopting traits from their neighbors. My cells don't seek out these traits and they do not seem to have a mechanism for refusing them. I like to think I have more power and autonomy than that, and if the biological metaphor ended here it would only mirror human experience very loosely.

The metaphor is deeper, however. If we follow the fate of a horizontally acquired gene, a type of cellular autonomy emerges over a long timeframe. Horizontal gene acquisition is unfiltered and random, but selection is involved in the maintenance of these genes. A cell can delete genes from its genome at any time, and the criteria it uses are described in ways that sound as subjective as the criteria for human choices. For instance, the cell deletes horizontally acquired genes that fail to "provide a meaningful function" (Ochmann, 2000). When the trait encoded by a gene is no longer meaningful to the cell, the gene is deleted.

This gene selection doesn't seem like the kind of process in which unthinking, unconscious cells could engage. It doesn't sound like the type of precise, logical and definable system we would expect from cells. There is no precise rubric and there are no defined criteria which determine whether a horizontally acquired gene will be maintained or deleted. The selection is situational, context-dependent and seemingly subjective.

The entire cycle of horizontal gene acquisition and deletion is quite different from the way I, as a young science student, expected biology to operate. Cells trade pieces of the stuff that defines them, thereby meshing with one another in a manner that blurs their individual identities and fades their boundaries. To further add to this imprecision and unpredictability, when any one of those boundary-less cells no longer finds meaning in its newly acquired gene, the cell simply deletes it. If I heard this behavior described to me without an indication that it is a cellular process, I would assume that it's on the irrational end of the spectrum of human behavior. My most concrete source of identity, it turns out, is porous and malleable, latching onto anything in its environment that suits it, and when those things no longer serve it, they're simply abandoned.

When I was five years old, my parents took me to my first Pittsburgh Symphony Orchestra concert. It was a day-time concert designed specifically for children, and the auditorium was smaller than the one they normally used for performances. The audience was close enough to the musicians that we could see the rosin dust puffing off of their bows and we could watch the transforming expressions on their faces, morphing to match the tone of the music. It was my first concert, and it was the first of many. I'd never before seen a violin, a cello, a trombone, a tuba or really any other instrument except for the guitars, keyboards, drums and tambourines I saw each Sunday in our church's worship band. About a minute into the very first piece, I noticed a particular sound. It was deep, occupying a low register. It was full and I felt like it completely surrounded me. It had a resonance that I could feel and not only hear, and a vibrancy that I simply couldn't ignore. At the time, I had none of these words to describe that sound, and I was at a loss to describe why I was so drawn to it. All I knew was that even then, as a five-year-old attending her first classical music concert, it sparked something in me.

I could tell which part of the stage that sound was coming from, and I asked my mom, stretching upward to whisper in her ear during the performance, what *those* beautiful instruments were called. She told me those were the cellos.

After the concert, I asked my mom if we could go up front to see a cello up close, and we made our way toward the stage. It was a casual midday concert and the musicians were prepared to interact one-on-one with the audience members, most of us children. One of the cellists saw us coming toward the edge of the stage and brought her cello over for me to see. I could smell the rich scent of the polished wood, and I touched the body of the instrument, feeling the grain of the wood and its delicate but strong structure. The strings were thick and strong, the bridge held up by their tension in a balance that somehow seemed simultaneously precarious and indestructible.

On our way home, I told my mom I wanted to play a cello one day. We waited a few years, until I was tall enough to carry a cello, strong enough to press down on the powerful strings and mature enough to understand that I needed to practice every day in order to make lessons worthwhile. Over those few intervening years I mentioned cellos often, never interested in any other instrument, always wanting to take any chance I was given to listen to cello music or go to cello concerts.

When we brought home my first cello, I felt like I was floating. Learning the basics of the instrument was a struggle of course, but I didn't mind the pain in my fingers as I developed calluses or the frustration I felt when I struggled to play in tune. It all felt worth it because I was finally playing the cello.

By the time I reached high school, I was practicing my cello for two hours every day, competing for seats in regional orchestras and thoroughly loving every minute of it. I felt magnetized by the sound of the instrument every time I heard it, even in the times when I was frustrated with the difficulty of playing it. The spark was still there, the one that had been ignited when I was five, and music was a means of accessing parts of my personality, my brain and my emotions that I had no other means of accessing.

When I was playing at this level, though, I felt an internal tension. I heard every week at youth group about the importance of finding my identity in Christ and not in activities, abilities, interests or desires. I wondered about the time I spent playing the cello: was God jealous of that time? Was this a selfish pursuit? Was it my pride and my sinful nature that drove me to play? Was I simply chasing validation and recognition? By the time I reached high school, I knew that I didn't want to make a career out of cello performance. Science had been my first and enduring interest and I liked the employment prospects for graduating chemistry majors a lot more than those for graduating cello performance majors.

I wondered what the purpose of music was for me. What was my end game? It felt wasteful to spend my time pursuing music, but I couldn't deny how important playing the cello was to me. When I played, I felt as though I was opening a release valve in my soul: any confusion, any self-hatred, any feelings of inadequacy — all of it just slowly diminished while I was playing. I couldn't rationalize it or explain it, but it was undeniably meaningful to me.

I continued regularly playing in ensembles during college. Several months after I graduated, I noticed my cello case standing in the corner of my bedroom and I saw a light coating of dust on the top of it. My first feeling was guilt: how could I have let all of this time go by without embracing my passion? Playing the cello was an activity I used to love. It was the instrument that used to ground me and center me and give a voice to the thoughts and feelings that I had no other way of expressing. Now, that instrument was simply collecting dust in my bedroom.

I unlatched the case, spread a thick layer of rosin on my

bow and took out my cello. I unfolded my music stand, took out a book of some go-to cello solos and I played. This became a ritual I'd repeat every few months or so when I would notice that guilt-inducing layer of dust accumulating on the top of my cello case. I did this for a few years, each time continuing to play for as long as my soft now-unconditioned fingertips would allow.

It was different, though. Somewhere along the line, something changed. I still loved the sound of my cello and I still loved the way it felt to play, but my cello simply didn't play the same role that it used to play. I had developed other means of expression. By this point in my life, I'd started writing, beginning to fill the pages of composition notebooks with personal reflections, childhood memories and descriptions of biological phenomena that had become meaningful and inspiring to me. I'd come to find in writing that sense of deep expression, emotional release and personal contentment that I used to feel every time I played my cello. Maybe it's just that I'd substituted other interests and activities for playing it, or maybe it was that the cello took me as far as it could take me. Regardless, it no longer felt like the irreplaceable personal release valve it once had been.

The story of me and my cello is highly particular and personal. Its details cannot be generalized; other people hear the sound of cello music without having the reaction I had. Plenty of others play musical instruments for myriad reasons and might not feel the sense of deep expression I felt or the sense that a metaphorical internal release valve was opening up. However, each of us has something we find meaningful. These particularities become integrated into our identities. It's difficult for me to predict what I will find meaningful. I cannot always identify rational explanations for the meaning and purpose I find and it often seems arbitrary. Unless I'm paying attention to my own inner voices, it's quite possible I'll miss it. These pieces of my identity come into my life from my environment, my inter-actions and my experiences, and they can shape and trans-form me if I let them. When they inevitably and inexplicably lose their meaning, or when they've simply run their course, they'll fall away. No matter how seemingly frivolous, insig-nificant or arbitrary, these sources of identity have the power to ground us, center us and transform us. When I was a high school-aged youth group kid, I didn't know I had the freedom to make this statement, but I now know it to be true: any God who would jealously require me to strip myself of my diverse, specific and personal sources of iden-tity and meaning is a God I'm uninterested in worshipping.

I can easily list the logical sources of my identity. I find meaning and purpose in a number of predictable, reasona-ble sources. My list would include my relationship with my husband, my work as a research scientist, the connection I have with my family, and the friendships I've made in my community. Everything on this list gives me a sense of meaning; a sense that what I'm doing in my life has value that extends beyond me. All of this is good, healthy and helpful. A problem arises, however, if I limit myself to find-ing meaning *only* in these sources of identity, clinging so tightly to the things I can rationally explain as my sources of identity, meaning and purpose that I miss the other sources that are available all around me.

The picture of identity that is displayed in biology in-spires me to think of my own identity differently. Biology portrays identity as a transforming, evolving property, ra-ther than an unchanging and static quality. What if I see my own identity as something that can transform? As an evangelical college student, desperate to find my identity in Christ, I thought that my identity was singular and that finding sources of meaning and purpose in anything other than Christ would detract from my identity in Christ. My identity was a kaleidoscope and I was trying to preserve one single image at the end of the chamber, my knuckles whitening as I resisted my curiosity and my interests, the very forces driving me to turn the kaleidoscope and grow. My life isn't static and it doesn't remain the same throughout circumstances. My life is instead a constantly transforming landscape of circumstances, capabilities and relationships, and I will serve myself well to find a sense of identity that is resilient enough to transform along with that landscape.

Sometimes my meaning, purpose and identity transform in response to a new idea—I read an article or a book, listen to a radio show or have a conversation and I feel a spark. That spark, which feels so meaningful to me in that moment, may later fade. My task is to continue searching in my surroundings after it fades, and just as my cells take up elements of identity from their environments, I have the opportunity to latch onto the new things I find that give me the sense of meaning, purpose and grounding that I'm looking for.

The elements of my identity, meaning and purpose stay with me for as long as they serve a meaningful function. If it means something to me, then it becomes a part of me. So, if it produces something good and useful for me, then it remains a part of me. However, if it crushes me, silences me, invalidates me or represses me, then it is not me, and if I release it, no longer claiming it as my identity, it will fall away over time.

Our cells' filter of meaningful function is a natural process of separating what is useful from what is inconsequential, removing that which is of no use and maintaining that which provides meaning, identity and life. It's a functional and natural process, and it's not logical or predictable. Our cells do not carefully select their sources of identity, but they absorb anything they find. It's a lot like the pattern I followed as a kid who was fascinated, magnetized and enthralled by the deep resonant sound that cellos make. I was finding my meaning and identity in the particularities of my experiences, and I was hanging onto anything I found to be meaningful.

This filtration process, the selection of what is meaningful, is a type of judgment. It's a judgment that originates internally and is fundamentally different from the externally imposed judgment I feared as a young evangelical. It's a revelation, a manifestation of what is true. When an element no longer provides a meaningful function, that element will eventually be lost. This is a form of judgment that doesn't come on a final day, and it doesn't consist of a tallying, a reckoning or a closing of the Book of Life. This is a judgment that comes day by day, and happens naturally and internally.

When I read the words of Jesus now, coming across his references to judgment, I can imagine the possibility that he's not fear-mongering. Maybe he's not talking about the judgment throne of God and our eventual ominous reckoning with the creator. Maybe he's not referring to a final test of character that will reveal our true identities and determine our eternal fates. The biological filter of meaningful function teaches me that judgment is an ongoing process and that it occurs here in this earthly life. It's not just a preparation for the afterlife. Judgment is the revelation of my constantly evolving identity, redefined and transformed day by day.

I find peace and comfort in this reimagination of judgment. As a transforming person, at times I will feel unstable, continuously changed by my environment. But the instability is nothing to fear. In fact, it's healthy. It's my nature. Constant transformation is the story echoed throughout my biology, down to my very cells. I'm continually changed by what surrounds me. My unfolding, transforming, emerging, impossible-to-pin-down identity is not a sign of weakness or inadequacy. Quite the opposite. This evolving identity is an undeniable sign of dynamic, abundant life.

6

KNOWING GOD

When I asked Jesus into my heart at the seasoned age of three, I already knew a lot about him. We talked about Jesus every day at home. I was taught how to pray as soon as I learned to speak in sentences, and from that point forward, prayer was a normal part of my everyday life. In my family, at home and at church, we said that praying was simply talking to God, and we talked casually, as though he were right there in the room with us. Every Sunday was dedicated to Jesus. At church, we sang about Jesus, listened to stories about Jesus and closed our eyes to shut out distractions and talk to Jesus. We believed that God and Jesus were in charge of everything. They were the ones we thanked and the ones we petitioned every time we needed help.

I even knew what Jesus looked like. I could pick him out on the pages of my Picture Bible. He was the one with pale white skin and crystal blue eyes, his gentle face framed with center-parted shoulder-length cascading brown waves of well-conditioned hair. I'd never met him, but I knew him. I knew his bright eyes, his smile, and the warm and gentle looks he gave to the children who were always gathered around him in those pictures.

I probably wouldn't have asked Jesus into my heart if I hadn't already known what he was like. I needed an image, and in my home and my church, I was surrounded by representations of that image. This image, my understanding of Jesus, remained essential to me in the years that followed. My Sunday school lessons taught me about Jesus and God, and the lessons grew in detail and depth as the years progressed. I learned God's traits and I learned how to deduce God's interests based on biblical evidence. In the children's classes I attended during our church services each week, we discussed what Jesus would do if he went to our schools, was friends with our friends and lived in our neighborhoods. We answered questions about how Jesus would treat his annoying little sister, and how Jesus would respond to his parents when they told him to clean his room. In high school, our discussions shifted to focus on what Jesus would say about the length of our skirts, how Jesus would respond when his friends bragged about trying alcohol for the first time, or what Jesus would do if someone flirted with him.

Throughout adolescence and young adulthood, even though the topics of our discussions changed, our focus remained the same. We wanted to know God. Specifically, we wanted to discern the traits and qualities of our God. At youth group meetings, at college ministry meetings and at adult small group meetings, we spent our time and energy trying to determine how Jesus would live if he were alive today. We debated whether Jesus would go on vacation to Jamaica or would only spend his vacation time volunteering to go on mission trips. We discussed what type of job Jesus might have, how much money Jesus would spend on a car, and what type of home life Jesus would have. Our questions changed with each new phase of life, but our underlying motive stayed the same. We wanted to know what God was like. I believed my God to be incapable of being ambivalent. Instead, I was convinced that he had specific opinions about everything I would do, from my clothing and music choices to my employment and family choices. If my God was powerful enough to create and sustain the universe, I reasoned, then he was powerful enough to have an opinion about everything I would do.

Like any middle- or high-schooler, I wondered what my future might hold. I didn't just wonder, however; I was deeply terrified of getting it wrong. I believed that God had a specific plan for my life: a version of my life where I would make all the right choices and select all the holiest options. God's plan, in my mind, would include an ideal college, ideal major, ideal roommate, ideal friends, ideal spouse and ideal career. I believed in a God who had very specific opinions, and it was up to me to discern them.

I believed in an intervening omnipotent God, a God who is in control of everything in the universe. I wanted him to be on my side. The more I could align my prayers with God's interests, I believed, the more likely God would be to answer those prayers. My God was an intervening God and I believed he would step into space and time in order to alter the course of my life, provided my prayers were fervent enough and I was righteous enough. I believed in a God who was responsive, and if he chose to do so, he could heal diseases, fill bank accounts and fix broken relationships. There were certain kinds of prayers, however, that I believed God wouldn't answer. God would ignore selfish prayers. He would only answer the prayers that aligned with his own desires. Discerning God's desires was important to me not just as a religious practice, but because it could make the difference between sickness and health and between prosperity and financial ruin.

I was an evangelical, so I was convinced that it wasn't just for the sake of my own faith that I sought to define God and discern his desires. I knew I couldn't possibly evangelize others to believe in a God I couldn't define. In my church, we searched for a narrative of a God who could bring order and redemption to the world which we believed to be degenerating and sinful. We made succinct lists of things God would or wouldn't do, and we named God's priorities, traits and characteristics. This was our way of justifying our faith to doubters and of selling our faith to potential believers. Evangelism, an essential component of our religious expression, was only possible if we presented a concise, well-defined image of God.

Our biblical discussions, debates and analyses were all hypothetical, but I pursued them as means of building my faith. Hebrews 11 begins with a definition of faith: "Faith is the assurance of things hoped for, the conviction of things not seen." Defining, clarifying and substantiating my unseen God was the purpose of my faith. My goal was to find this substance, and to build my life upon it. Carrying out these thought experiments and extrapolating these biblical references to my own life situations was a process that felt akin to alchemy. I was transforming an ethereal, elusive spiritual concept into something certain; something that had substance.

In times of transition or uncertainty, I tend to grasp even more desperately for things that are clearly defined. In the four years I spent as an undergraduate, I was gently introduced to partial independence and it felt newly chaotic and uncertain. I'd been taught to worship a God who cared about every detail of my existence, and my everyday life felt like a continuous chain of pivotal decisions. My daily choices seemed highly consequential, even though they truly weren't. My pivotal decisions ranged from selecting a roommate to scheduling my classes to choosing which

Christian campus fellowship I would attend. In my mind, there were infinite possibilities in my future, but there was only one future that God had planned for me. My task was to discern God's perfectly planned path.

I wasn't alone in this search, but my Christian campus group was full of students who were also convinced that their semester course selection could impact the very fabric of space-time. We fed off of each other's quest for discernment, spiraling into an odd competition to "hear God" most clearly and to "choose God's will" most consistently. The irony was lost on us, but these efforts that we believed were honoring to God were actually rooted in thinly veiled self-obsession.

I sat across from one of my college ministry friends at a tiny round Starbucks table one spring Wednesday afternoon. She and I were prayer partners this particular semester. We believed that if we mentioned specific details in our prayers, that would make them stronger, which was a great excuse to spend our "prayer partnership" time mostly complaining and gossiping.

I had just finished sharing my prayer request with her, and I flopped back against my chair with a defeated sigh. She was quick to assure me that "no concern is too small for God!" Her eyes were wide and unblinking. Her neck craned forward over our matching pair of skinny vanilla lattes, her face inches from mine. She cocked her head to the side, contorting her face in a look of passion and eagerness. The barista, behind the counter, watching us from a distance, must have been certain my friend was telling me about her new crush. Her voice was hushed and earnest, passionate and sincere. "God, who created the entire world...God cares about *you*. He will direct your path." Her eyes flared wide open with "entire world" and then retreated back beneath a furrowed brow as she softly elongated "*you*." She knew she wasn't telling me anything I hadn't already been told. She was repeating what both of us had been taught since infancy. Her dramatic facial expressions were just her way of driving the familiar point home. For us, this was simple logic. The God we believed in would care about his creation, and humanity, we naively and egocentrically assumed, is at the pinnacle of creation. So of course, we reasoned, God cared enough about us to show us the best way to live.

There was something about this train of thought, though, that never quite made sense to me. We weren't just talking about a God who cares about humans. I'd love to believe in that God. We were talking about a God who cares about my problems, in particular. I knew better than anyone that my problems were *not* problems. For example, the prayer request I was sharing with her, which was my biggest conundrum at that moment, was the choice between switching my major to biochemistry, or just sticking to chemistry as I'd planned from the beginning. Switching would cost me some money, because it would mean I'd have to pay tuition for one summer class that year, and that I would have to forego a large portion of my planned summer income. But on the plus side, I'd probably be a little better prepared to apply to the graduate programs I had in mind. Sticking with chemistry meant no summer classes, no summer tuition payments, and more time to work and save up for the fall semester. On the down side, though, I would be running the risk of an uncomfortable moment at my grad school admission interviews, when I might be asked about the gap in my transcript where advanced biochemistry courses should be. It's an indication of the comfort and privilege I enjoyed during my childhood and adolescence that this was the most pivotal and consequential decision I'd made in my entire life.

"God has a perfect plan for your life!" Her eyes were now glittering, wide with wonder as tiny pools of tears started to form inside her lower eyelids.

She was talking about a God who was the perfect boyfriend. Her God was a perfect listener. He was always showering her with gifts, always affirming her and spending time with her. The very idea of this God comforted her. This was a God who cared about every part of her life, no matter how mundane or insignificant.

The idea of this kind of God never really comforted me, though. This God confused and frustrated me. How could God care this much about my course selection but allow kids to be abused in their homes right in my own neighborhood? How could God be deeply concerned about which college ministry boy I'd sit with in the dining hall, yet fail to intervene to help a young mom across town pay her rent this month? A God who would solve my problems, which really are *not* problems, but would neglect vastly more consequential, painful and devastating problems wouldn't be a caring God. That God would be a villain.

As an evangelical kid, I had no lack of familiarity with Bible stories. My biblical education was supposed to be the anchor that would secure me in my faith, preventing me from considering other spiritual paths. For me though, the Bible provided more questions than answers. Biblical texts seemed to each describe radically different characteristics of God. Instead of solidifying the foundation of my faith, this literal interpretation of the Bible actually led me to believe that God has multiple personalities. Not only this, but most of those personalities would belong to a terrible boyfriend.

Sometimes the God I read about in the Bible seemed impulsive, sending she-bears out of the woods to maul a group of kids just because they had insulted Elisha (II Kings 2:23-24). Other times, God was two-faced, trying to kill his servant Moses, seemingly to test his strength and determination (Exodus 4:24-26). God was also not above playing mind games, telling Abraham to offer his son as a sacrifice, and then calling off the profoundly violent plan seconds before Abraham obediently stabbed his own child through the heart (Genesis 22:1-12). God could even be annoyingly indirect, dodging questions. When Moses asked for some simple information—who are you?—God replied "I am who I am" (Exodus 3:14). It's a cop-out, a response that isn't a helpful answer.

In other biblical scenarios, God seemed arrogant and manipulative, mandating seemingly senseless laws that allowed for no exceptions. Failing to "keep the Sabbath" was punishable by death for the Israelites (Exodus 31:14). If "God is love" (I John 4:8), how could God be this harsh, refusing to accommodate emergencies or special situations? Other laws established bizarre and illogical litmus tests. If an Israelite woman was suspected of having an affair, she would be forced to drink water mixed with dust from the tabernacle floor. If it didn't make her sick, she was declared innocent and if she became ill, she was declared guilty (Numbers 5:11-31). I'd been taught that God never changes, but the stories I read in the Bible told the story of a constantly changing God. The personalities behind each of these stories, each having its own form of absurdity, conflicted with each other and confused me. The harder I looked, the more impossible it seemed for me to know what God was really like.

Across that tiny round Starbucks table on that Wednesday afternoon, though, was a person who knew exactly what God was like. Her eyes were calm and confident, passionate and relaxed. It seemed that every Bible story she read simply confirmed and clarified the image of God that she already saw. For me though, the more I learned about God, the foggier his image became. The more my clarity faded, the more I wondered: if my faith in God was this tenuous, was it even worthwhile to continue fighting for it? My image of God was the bedrock of my belief and with that image now shrouded in confusion, my faith felt more and more fraudulent every day.

I believed I had two options: I could either dig in my heels, squeeze my eyes tight and just try to believe harder, or I'd have to drop the pursuit of Christian faith altogether. With this dichotomy filling my view, I entered into a limbo period. It was a phase of rapid oscillation between committed, hopeful faith and depressive disorientation. Maybe it was because of my personality, maybe it was my culture, or maybe it was the fact I was a millennial twenty-something, but I existed in consistent depression and disorientation rather than in hope.

My disorientation and depression heightened my desperation to find something — anything — that was concrete. Disillusioned by theological exploration, I was drawn toward the certainty and predictability of the natural sciences. Natural science fields are known for their reliability and clarity. The scientific method is rigorous, and it's a technique intentionally designed to safeguard against misunderstanding. But the unknown is the engine that drives the progress of scientific research. As a young student of science, it was easy to assume that scientists work in a realm of concrete facts and incontrovertible conclusions. But this was simply due to the fact that when I was a student, the examples I saw had been hand-selected and the explanations had already been tested to a point of tremendous reliability.

My textbooks were filled with neatly organized chapter subheadings and perfectly placed sidebar examples, but the practice of laboratory research science was not like this. It was only as a student that I had the luxury of performing tried-and-true laboratory protocols that had already been optimized. In research labs, I collaborated with other students and scientists to create our own patchwork protocols for investigating phenomena that had never been probed before in that particular way. We spent our time sifting through published journal articles, cutting and pasting protocols until we felt comfortable enough to give it a try. In order to get started with a project, we relied on educated guesses and intuition. We tried one approach, it usually failed, we began to troubleshoot, tweaked some parameters and tried again. We repeated this process until it either worked or we decided it wasn't worth it and we took an entirely different path. When it finally worked, sometimes we knew why, and sometimes we didn't know why. When we didn't know why, we took it as a clue directing us toward our next project. Unanswered questions were open doors that beckoned us to continue asking questions until a link was elucidated.

This is still the model that I use in laboratory research. Every answer simply raises an entirely new set of questions. As soon as scientific research answers a particular question, the research community moves on to new questions. Science, as a discipline, is always at the boundary of human certainty. As researchers, we're not interested in what is clear and established, but we are always engaging with our questions. Our confusions, our doubts and our uncertainties interest us much more than the answers do, because the questions show us where opportunities lie.

Biology, my chosen field, is the investigation of life. Biological investigation is inherently awkward, because as biologists, we study ourselves. We, living human beings, are the subject of our own study, along with all other living things in our universe. A preliminary step in the investigation of life is to define life, and since we're already quite familiar with it—in fact being it ourselves—we might expect that it would be easy to reach such a definition. Everyone knows what life is. Even preschoolers can distinguish between living and non-living things. Although everyone knows what life is, however it is highly challenging to define life. We don't realize this until we set aside our intuitive definitions and search for precise language by which to define life. It's then that we realize our language is imprecise and our metaphors fall short.

It's not for lack of trying that we have so much trouble reaching a working definition for life. Biologists make sincere efforts to establish a definition for life, engaging in lively discussions at scientific conferences. These discussions usually involve a repeated cycle: one biologist presents a possible definition for life, that definition is then challenged by the other biologists in the room, who highlight its weaknesses and holes; a new, revised definition is proposed, and the cycle repeats in perpetuity. All of this is done in an attempt to generate a definition of life that leaves no gray areas, no uncertainties, and no confusion. These biologists make concise lists of life's characteristics, but as soon as a new list is made, they realize they've excluded something that seems like it is alive, or they've included something that seems inanimate.

Daniel Koshland is a biologist who was in one of these rooms, debating with other biologists as they all desperately and earnestly tried to arrive at a definition for life (Koshland 2002). It probably sounded like a debate, but they all had the same goal: to identify a concise and functional definition of life. Koshland later wrote about this discussion, demonstrating its deep challenges:

"What is the definition of life? I remember a conference of the scientific elite that sought to answer that question. Is an enzyme alive? Is a virus alive? Is a cell alive? After many hours of launching promising balloons that defined life in a

135

sentence, followed by equally conclusive punctures of these balloons, a solution seemed at hand: 'The ability to reproduce — that is the essential characteristic of life' said one statesman of science. Everyone nodded in agreement that the essential of a life was the ability to reproduce, until one small voice was heard. 'Then one rabbit is dead. Two rabbits — a male and female — are alive but either one alone is dead.' At that point, we all became convinced that although everyone knows what life is, there is no simple definition of life."

In the article, Koshland goes on to offer a solution. He suggests that we can define life with seven "pillars" of its characteristics. This definition is thorough enough to include all the forms of life most seemingly dissimilar to humans (bacteria, archaea, etc.) without including things that are clearly inanimate. The pillars are Program, Improvisation, Compartmentalization, Energy, Regeneration, Adaptability and Seclusion.

This definition of life is finally expansive enough to include all known life forms, but it presents a new challenge. Each of the pillars must be interpreted. They are loose, multifaceted and open to interpretation. Their gray areas are abundant and expansive. This definition for life is not the concise, clear, concrete kind we would expect from the natural sciences, but it's the best we can do.

The challenge of defining life is humbling and, like any riddle, it can captivate us and push us to keep tinkering with our definitions until we find something functional. But the biological community is largely unfazed by the challenge. The absence of a working definition has not stopped the progress of biology research. We can still investigate life, even though we can't define it. We have analyzed countless cellular components, developed disease-fighting medications, learned to care for our natural habitats and promoted human health and longevity, all without a clear definition of life. At no point in the course of biological research have we had a clear definition of the object of our study, but that hasn't stopped us from studying it.

Each new finding provides a measure of clarity. Biological research provides concrete conclusions. This type of clarity, however, does not untangle the tremendous mystery undergirding the object of the study. This mystery — what is life? — is not one that we have the tools for unraveling. Scientific investigation is a world in which mystery and clarity are not opposites, but are dance partners. Scientific understanding always coexists with mystery, concrete knowledge intertwined with grand absurdities at every turn.

Scientific exploration focuses on miniscule aspects of the grand mystery of life. We explore, all the while knowing that we are, at least in part, feeling around in the dark. No matter how many observations we make, or how many pathways, mechanisms, modes of development and causes of behavior we discover, there is something about their grand sum that remains mysterious. The drive toward survival, the persistent formation of new life, the incredible ability of living things to adapt to our surroundings — these are all mysteries that cannot be fully encompassed by measurement, quantification and identification of causes. The measurable aspects of nature are themselves undergirded by mysteries that we do not yet have means of probing.

Uncertainty is the engine that drives scientific progress forward. This progress, however, is best seen not as an effort to eradicate uncertainty, but as a persistent engagement with uncertainty. We work always at the edges of our current knowledge. This requires patience to develop tools for investigating what we cannot yet define or understand, eagerness to engage with doubt and willingness to re-examine accepted conclusions when our data challenges them.

As a graduate student, I learned firsthand just how much patience is required for this type of investigation. About one-third of my way through my graduate program, I neared the first major milestone in my program: my first oral exam. Passing this exam was my only remaining requirement to receive a master's degree, and my peers regarded this exam with such reverence that I was convinced if I could pass it, I could consider myself a serious and legitimate science student.

This oral exam would be different from any of my exams up to that point. Instead of being tested on my mastery of textbook material, I'd be tested on my own independent research findings. After delivering an oral presentation detailing my lab work, I'd be questioned by a committee of professors in my department. Their questions could pertain to absolutely anything, and the duration would be as long as they chose. It was an exam that I couldn't specifically study for, but one that would draw on the entirety of my science education.

As this oral exam neared, my anxiety heightened. I knew I hadn't been lazy. I knew I had studied the basics. For 2.5 years, I'd been working at my lab bench all day, performing procedures and conducting analyses. Despite all of this, however, I had yet to test a single hypothesis.

I had no results.

At the start of my graduate program, I set out to study one specific protein. This particular protein had been discovered in human cells and was quickly assigned a category, based on its amino acid sequence. The protein had not yet been studied further, so very little was known about its role. Educated guesses had been made about its function, based solely on its amino acid sequence, but those guesses had not been confirmed at the time that I began my work.

The very idea of this project excited me. I was being given the opportunity to study a component of the human tapestry — a physical part of me, and of every other human being, a piece that is part of the puzzle that makes us human. No one in the entire world had yet unlocked its secrets. I had the chance to crack a tiny portion of the human code and to fit one miniscule piece into the grand and mysterious human biological puzzle.

During my first week of graduate school, my research advisor sat down with me to discuss the "very first step" of my project, which I assumed to be the kind of task I'd finish in a few weeks. He explained that in order to determine the protein's function, I'd need to produce a large amount of it, and also find a way to purify it. The procedures I'd use would be standard, common biological procedures.

Specifically, I'd be using bacterial cells as factories for protein production.

This method of protein production and purification had long been well-established and extensively optimized, so I expected I'd complete this protein production step in no time, and soon be ready to move on to use experiments to test my hypotheses about the protein's function in human cells.

The protein I had chosen to study was one that naturally occurs in humans, but does not occur in bacteria. My task was to produce large quantities of the protein using bacterial cells as though they were protein factories. This can be challenging, even impossible at times, because a cell's machinery often specifically facilitates production of its own natural proteins, but does not facilitate production of foreign proteins. Cells contain natural proteins called chaperones. These chaperones are "helper" proteins that facilitate protein production. Each type of cell has a unique ensemble of chaperones, so human chaperones are not the same as bacterial chaperones, and often these distinct proteins are not interchangeable with one another. The chaperones inherent to these bacterial cells, the ones I was attempting to use as factories, mismatched the protein I was attempting to produce, and the mismatch disrupted the protein production process. The disruption was so great that now, after 2.5 years of trying to produce protein, I had nothing to show for it.

All this time, I kept trying, troubleshooting, tweaking my methods and trying again, but it didn't work. Each time it failed, I tried an alternative method, hoping to rescue the failed protein production. None of these alternatives worked, so I kept going right back to the beginning of the process and starting over. None of my efforts were successful and now, months before my oral exam, I had nothing to show for my efforts.

If I'd been constructing and testing hypotheses for these 2.5 years, even if I'd been observing surprising, strange or insignificant results, I would have been able to accept those outcomes more easily. I would have presented my negative results to my exam committee and proposed my alternative hypotheses and my experimental means of testing them. But none of this was the case. My failure was so monumental that I hadn't even reached the point where I could begin conducting experiments and testing hypotheses. I had not yet even succeeded in making the tools I'd need for my investigation.

I was learning the implications of novel explorations. Research, by definition, is an exploration of the unknown. As a scientist, this was my first interaction with realities that were not yet characterized — realities for which tools of investigation had not yet been developed. In order to forge into this uncharted biological territory, I'd first need to find a way to approach it. Before I could frame questions that would make sense, I had to learn the appropriate vocabulary.

My exam committee understood this much better than I did, and at the end of their line of questioning, reassured me. They explained that it would be naïve and foolish, when investigating a novel piece of the biological puzzle, not to expect a period of trial-and-error. Confusion and a vast collection of inconclusive results are often the only outcomes of an initial study.

Biology is the study of the undefinable: life. It progresses through patient, persistent and curious engagement with the unknown. The answers that biology provides always raise brand-new questions of their own. The undefinable mystery of life — of which we are a part — is not directly addressed by the scientific method; we can only approach it through more circuitous routes. Concise language and clear definitions are not sufficient to encompass the mystery that undergirds life, but instead we must use multifaceted complex guidelines that are open to interpretation, like Koshland's seven pillars of life. Nonetheless, scientific exploration continues, a bold effort to engage with the mysteries of life, and we patiently search for small corners of clarity within an unknown and mysterious landscape.

In a surprising way, recognizing the uncertainty and mystery that I found at the heart of scientific investigation gave me the environment that I needed. The murkiness gave me the freedom to be wrong, not because of sloppiness or failure to adhere to the scientific method, but because I was in uncharted territory. It gave me the freedom to ask all the questions I could think of, not just the questions that could support my hypothesis. It gave me the freedom to engage with my doubt and uncertainty. Once I knew that I was engaging with something infinitely explorable, I was freed from the fear of asking the wrong questions. Scientific investigation showed me that the presence of mystery need not silence interrogations, but can evoke infinite questions.

As a young evangelical, I assumed that certainty and mystery were opposites. I believed they were mutually exclusive and that if I couldn't maintain clarity, certainty and precision in my beliefs about the nature of God, I'd become lost in confusion. Biology, however, presented me with a third option, beyond these binary opposing poles: exploration. In the mind of the explorer, mystery and clarity can coexist.

Science taught me to keep exploring, *especially* when I'm uncertain. It taught me that if I can't define the thing I'm exploring, then I can be confident my exploration is worthwhile. I can expect that new experiences and new discoveries might alter the definitions, paradigms and models I've already developed, and that a strong conclusion will always be a malleable one. This explorational approach to God involves synthesizing my experiential knowledge and traditional understandings. It requires me to keep in mind that traditional understandings were developed by humans who were simply doing their best to describe mysteries using the metaphors and images available to them. New evidence always has the power to shift even our strongest paradigms, replace our clearest definitions and modify our most predictive theories.

I used to be afraid of this type of faith. I thought that honoring my experiential knowledge would be selfish and that my resulting faith would be flimsy. The only kind of faith I wanted was the kind that preliminarily defined its object. In biological exploration, however, new data has the power to alter established models. If we preliminarily develop definitions for life, we are likely to close ourselves off, destroying our ability to observe nature with honesty. Biological exploration is a quest to understand something of which we, as humans, are a part, and something that we cannot define. This remarkable pursuit persists by treating mystery respectfully and treating data honestly.

If I read the biblical narratives about God with this explorational framework in mind, the texts seem to point me further toward a pursuit of understanding, rather than toward the certainty I used to desire. The Old Testament accounts of God tell me the story of humans doing their best to gain understanding of an ultimately inscrutable reality: God. They used the best tools that were available to them: the linguistic and storytelling tools that were prevalent in their communities. God is portrayed differently throughout these stories, like the image at the end of a kaleidoscope, transforming with each new situation and perspective, never settling on a final image, never selecting a superior image, but continually expanding in beauty and diversity. In the past, when I interpreted these texts as literal accounts, their meaning was obscured by my fear of uncertainty. They seemed to be contradictory accounts of a confusing God who has multiple personalities. Now, in light of my understanding of biological exploration, these accounts seem to celebrate the diversity of all the possible understandings of God. Throughout time and space, we continue to describe images, develop metaphors and create definitions of this mysterious God. We do this because it's the best we can do. These tools—telling stories, composing poetry or music, painting, sculpting or developing metaphors—are our means of exploration. None of these means will fully encompass the divine, but the mystery simply inspires me to keep exploring.

The God in the Bible is bigger than I ever acknowledged when I was an evangelical biblical literalist. The God I perceive now is a God that holds my attention. There will always be more to learn about this God. This is a God that keeps us always engaged. There will forever be brand-new images to see through the kaleidoscope, and the diversity and beauty of these images will always point to a mystery that is greater than what we can know. It is only in respecting and loving this perpetually unfolding image of God that I have found the sense of wonder and awe that I once tried to generate in myself as a young evangelical.

7

PURE AS SNOW

The swirly streaks intertwined to create infinite mazes on the wall. It's all I could see, but it was enough to keep me mesmerized. Sharp curved ridges of glossy white paint-coated plaster swirled around and in-between each other, tangling into knotted jumbles. Brand new plaster streaks emerged on the opposite side of every jumble, their origins untraceable. The emerging streaks went on to swirl, twirl and intertwine all over again. I was tired. I leaned my head into the corner. My forehead started to hurt right away, resting in the corner of these living room walls, plaster ridge imprints starting to form on my skin.

I had not been forgotten, and I'd been standing there for no more than about ten minutes, but I felt like I'd been standing in the corner for all eternity. I was seven years old, that age when time feels elastic, passing by unnoticed when I played soccer in the backyard but slowing to a crawl when I sat on the back bench seat of our family vehicle during a road trip. Standing in the corner, with nothing to look at but the plaster streaks and nothing to think about except the bad behavior that landed me there in the first place, the pace of time plodded along, even slower than a crawl.

"Dad? How much longer?"

I knew the rules. When I was sent to the corner, I was expected to stand there and remain quiet. I was tired though; my feet hurt and I was bored. I was willing to break the rules at this point.

"Dad?" I was a little louder this time. I knew I wasn't supposed to complain. In fact, I knew that every time I complained, my total time in the corner was lengthened by just a little bit.

"Dad!" Now I was shouting. "Do you even remember I'm here!?"

As soon as I heard his voice behind me, calm and firm, I turned my face away from the corner and saw him standing at the end of the hallway that led to the kitchen. His tone was even, as it always was.

"You know I have to punish you when you break the rules. I know you're there and I won't forget you." His mouth pursed as he finished the last sentence and his eyes squinted into a sympathetic, understanding smile. It was a look of encouragement, a look that told me to just hang in there and this punishment would be over very soon.

My family operated according to codes of conduct. It was a privilege to grow up in a household that had clearly defined, consistently enforced rules. Following a typical youngest-child pattern, I caught onto the rules early in life. I watched as my siblings were regularly reminded of the rules and punished when they disobeyed those rules. It was always clear to me that if I disrupted the family's codes of conduct, there would be consequences.

It was no surprise to me that I was sent to the corner. In fact, nearly every time I was punished as a kid, I knew to expect it beforehand. My parents administered punishment consistently, and I never sensed anger or even a high amount of emotion when they punished me. A few minutes prior to this particular trip to the corner, in the moment when I was disrespectfully snapping at my mom, I knew I was doing something wrong. Now, standing in the corner, it wasn't exactly the punishment itself that made me so upset. What upset me was the fact that I did something wrong in the first place. My bad behavior made me feel out of control. I didn't have the willpower to stop. To me, when I felt that my behavior was uncontrolled, that was a sign that *bad* wasn't just something I did, but something I was.

For my family, punishment always had a specific purpose. I was fortunate that my parents readily explained why my behavior had been unacceptable and I always knew the reason for any punishment I received. The reasons were specific — sometimes I needed to learn to be respectful, other times I had to be taught to share, other times they were teaching me never to lie. Before sending me here to the corner, my dad explained what he wanted me to do while I was there: think about what I'd done wrong and think about how I could avoid doing it again. I knew we'd revisit the conversation again later, as we always did each time I was punished. My dad or mom would ask me what I'd learned, and what my plan was for the next time. I had to know what I'd done wrong and have a plan to do better in the future, because regardless of the specific purpose of the punishment, my parents' ultimate goal was always the same. Their goal was to teach me self-control.

There was also another purpose for punishment in our house. It was through punishment that we believed we could be purified from our sin. My bad behavior — whether it was jealousy, anger, selfishness or dishonesty — didn't just break our family rules; it broke God's rules. We believed that we, along with all of humanity, were inherently sinful, fallen and separate from God. We believed the brutal, bloody and torturous death of sinless Jesus on the cross was God's way of punishing him instead of us, settling the score and making it possible for us to become pure. The sinless one was punished so that the sinful ones could become pure.

Our God was retributive and would only choose to spare us from damnation because of his grace and kindness. We believed in total human depravity, and that we could never deserve anything other than damnation. Within this framework, earthly punishment was God's way of purifying us so we would learn to accept his grace and be spared from the damnation we deserved. We believed the negative consequences of our actions were God's way of letting us learn the easy way so we could become purified and avoid our eventual damnation. If we foolishly resisted the lessons God was teaching us during our lives, we could expect to end up in hell for eternity. I saw my parents' punishment as a similarly gracious gesture. They were giving me the option of learning the easy way, and I believed they were protecting me from the real danger of experiencing the full consequences of my actions. The sooner I could learn to overcome my sinful nature and exhibit self-control, the sooner I'd be able to live in true freedom.

The first time I moved out of my parents' home was the week I started my freshman year of college. All three of us knew that things would be different. I was on my own now. Compliance with their rules was no longer expected, and enforcement of their rules was no longer appropriate. This was my first taste of independent adulthood. This was supposed to be the finish line I'd been working toward all along.

It did not, however, feel like a finish line. My daily struggles were the same as they had been before, except now they were a lot scarier. Now, I had no supervision. I still had the same selfishness I had as a kid. I still got angry,

I was still tempted to be lazy, I still struggled to be honest, I still prideful and jealous. I still had all those bad tendencies, except now I had no one to keep me in check.

I no longer kept a food diary by the time I got to college, the way I did as a preteen, but many of my nutritional record-keeping habits had become second nature by this point. I thought I had learned my lesson; my doctor was no longer concerned about my weight and I imagine I felt as comfortable in my body as any 18-year-old American female can. Although I was no longer actively, intentionally trying to change my body, my eating habits themselves still felt sinful. I still felt out of control when I ate, and I considered that out-of-control feeling to be gluttony. My eating habits became my chosen battlefield in the war I chose to wage against myself. I was convinced I should strive to somehow win this battle and gain self-control once and for all.

I never set a specific eating-related goal for myself other than to simply stop being gluttonous. The problem was that "gluttony," for me, never had a solid definition. In my head, there was never a distinction between gluttony and hunger or enjoyment. I'd been taught relentlessly that I was completely and thoroughly sinful at my core — that, like all humans, I was totally depraved — and that God's grace was my only hope of ever becoming anything but evil. With this belief front-and-center in my mind, I became suspicious of my own impulses, even those that were truly normal, healthy components of being a living human being.

My self-suspicion permeated more and more of my daily habits. I was terrified, not of an external danger, but of the evil that I believed to reside at my deepest core. I'd been taught that in order for me to improve upon my sinful nature, my heart would have to be purified by God. It was difficult for me to understand my heart, though, but my actions were concrete and quantifiable. And while a lot of my daily habits made me feel guilty, few of them were as quantifiable as my food-related habits. I believed that God hated all of my sins, and was just as furious with me for my anger, jealousy or deceitfulness as he was when I was gluttonous. My words, thoughts and intentions, however were not as easy to count as my calories. It was hard to know the difference between jealousy and ambition. It was hard to know the difference between anger and a love of justice. I'd convinced myself, though, that a person who is losing weight cannot possibly be a glutton, and I had a device that could tell me, in jumbo-sized digital numerals whether or not I was losing weight.

The arithmetic of food, with which I'd become deeply familiar just a few years earlier, was comforting. Numbers have concrete meanings and straightforward, universal operations. Managing these numbers gave me a sense of self-control. I summed the calories I consumed and subtracted the calories I burned based on the number of minutes I exercised. On the days when my calculations told me that I burned more than I consumed, I could easily convince myself I was in full control of my sinful, selfish impulses.

I constructed a budgeting system, and all I had to do in order to pay off my calorie debts was to save up my calorie allowance. It only took a bit of online searching for me to decide on a caloric balance that would theoretically result in weight loss. With that balance as my goal, I simply had to make the necessary transactions in order to strike that balance each day. Exercise felt like a way to punish myself for my gluttony and restricting my calorie intake felt like a way to increase my capacity for self-control.

While many of my daily habits and behaviors extended beyond myself and affected the people around me, eating was different. Eating and exercising could be completely isolated and personal. No apologies were necessary to correct what I saw as the damage that was done by my eating. I simply had to undo the caloric damage; a momentary weakness would not permanently mar my record. I could correct a mistake by simply spending an hour on the treadmill. It was harder to purify myself from other sins, but with food, I had ways to make it as though my failure had never even happened in the first place. I could have complete control.

It took a few years, but it eventually became clear that I had devised an impossible task for myself. When I first began equating weight loss with self-control, I was on the higher end of a healthy weight range, but as the number on the scale decreased and the protrusion of my hipbones increased, I neared the endpoint of healthy weight loss. For a few years, I'd been restricting my calories as much as I could and I'd developed a habit of purging, which I saw as a way to quickly undo caloric damage and earn a chance to start over. At first, the changes in my body were gradual and appeared to be healthy, but over time, my friends and family members' comments changed from congratulatory to concerned. I started experiencing GI pain on a regular basis, my hair began thinning rapidly, falling out in handfuls, I developed amenorrhea and I would shiver with cold even wearing long sleeves during the summer.

Even so, I still felt out of control. It didn't matter how low that number got, the one displayed in jumbo-sized numerals on my bathroom scale. I still felt impulsive in my eating. The looser my clothes became and the more gaunt my face appeared, the more terrified I was of getting stuck at an all-time low weight, and seeing the number on the scale stay constant. I needed to know I was losing weight in order to know I had self-control. Sharing that fear with my close friends was my path toward eventually ending this self-destructive quest for self-control. It was a sign that my weight loss was not goal-related but was an unending pursuit with no finish line.

The process of ending my self-destructive quest took time, of course because I'd come to rely on those daily scale readings for affirmation. I thought the continually decreasing numbers were proof that I was overcoming selfishness.

I thought I was taming my own sinful nature. I was convinced that I needed physical evidence in order to know that I was on the right track.

I felt trapped. It seemed that God had given me, along with the rest of humanity, an impossible task. We had been created selfish and sinful, I believed, but we were expected to overcome that sin. We were expected to be something that we were not. When I watched the number on the scale plummet, I was able to convince myself that I was overcoming my selfishness, learning to deny myself and to ignore my fleshly desires. Now, though, I'd shrunken myself as much as I could and I'd denied myself as much as I could, but I still felt selfishness—what I believed to be my sinful nature—inside of myself. I felt that I couldn't escape from my own sinful nature.

As a kid, I memorized a verse of the Bible every week, assigned during my children's class at Sunday church services. The Bible memory verse that remained most prominent in my mind, even when I was a college student, was Romans 3:23: "for all have sinned and fall short of the glory of God." I couldn't forget it even if I tried. If I would have learned this verse in isolation from the rest of the Bible, it would have seemed to be a simple reference to the finitude and frailty of humanity. I wasn't learning this verse in isolation. I was also learning verses like Romans 6:23, "for the wages of sin is death, but the free gift of God is eternal life in Christ Jesus our Lord." The eternal life that this verse mentions, given to those who believe in their hearts that Jesus is Lord (Romans 10:9) was elusive. My sin was tangible—quantifiable even, I thought—but my beliefs seemed abstract. I could never identify my beliefs as clearly as I could identify my sin. These messages, taken together, convinced me that my natural state as a sinner was both inescapable and unacceptable.

There are forms of life that are unconscious and unthinking and have no ability to make choices. At the height of my quest for domination over what I believed to be my sinful nature, the cell and molecular realms of life gave me a distinct sense of peace. At the time, I felt trapped by the impossible task that I believed God had given to humanity, but cells were living things that had never been given this task. They seemed to simply exist, and while I believed that God declared my behaviors damnable, cells and molecules were clearly free of any such indictment. At my core, I knew that I was part of the same natural tapestry that includes the microscopic realm, and I wanted to believe that I could access a measure of the simplicity of existence that I saw in biological systems. I wanted to believe that I could be free from my sinful nature, and instead, simply exist. This sense of simplicity of existence in biological systems magnetized me.

By sixth grade, I had identified my career ambition: medical research. The need for medical research has always been obvious to me. Our bodies break down, become diseased and suffer injuries. Quite a bit of work remains to be done in order to find cures and treatments for many of our diseases, even those that are common and deadly. The opportunity and need for medical research resonated with me when I was a middle and high-schooler and I decided to pursue a career path that would lead to medically related research. I was a chemistry major in college with a hope of unraveling disease causes and discovering ways of preventing diseases from arising in the first place.

Early on in my course of study, I learned about the

foundation of cellular function: the master molecule, DNA. Given the foundational, essential role of DNA as the basis of gene expression, a flaw in a DNA molecule creates profound reverberations, deeply impacting a person's traits. Every cell has, coiled up in its nucleus, a DNA molecule which is an identical copy of the DNA molecules that are coiled up in the nuclei of every other one of that body's cells. Each of these DNA molecules must engage in the correct chemical reactions at the correct time in the correct location at the correct rate for the correct duration in order to keep a person alive and healthy. Each of these parameters varies from one context to another, and is determined by a vast array of factors, including the cell type, the person's age, what they ate that day and how much they slept the night before. Gene expression is a finely tuned system, to say the very least.

Not only is the correctness of DNA essential for producing proteins via transcription and translation, but DNA is the template that a cell uses when it makes its own replacement. A cell doesn't last forever, and before it dies, it duplicates itself. A replacement cell is made during **mitosis**. DNA replication, which is the duplication of a cell's DNA molecule, is the very first step in mitosis. The cell uses its own DNA molecule as a template for duplication, so if left unaddressed, a lesion in a parent cell will be passed on to daughter cells. A problem in the DNA molecule does not only damage the cell it occupies, but it is destructive to every offspring cell that is produced for generations to come.

This is an incredibly delicate system, and when it breaks down, the ramifications are devastating. When one DNA molecule inside one single cell develops a **lesion**, that flaw affects the entire system. Disease and degeneration quickly follow when DNA lesions arise. DNA, the tiny, nearly invisible molecule that is coiled up inside every cell, has the power to completely destroy a life. Even the tiniest component of the system is indisputably capable of derailing the whole thing.

Biology is attractively concrete and quantifiable. Unlike the elusive solutions to social problems or the complicated dynamics of human behavior, biological problems can often be concisely diagnosed, treated and prevented. As a student of biology, I was drawn to the reliability of scientific prediction. I thought it would be possible to untangle cause-effect relationships with complete certainty, and with such predictability that science could be used to prevent new problems from arising in the first place.

When I graduated from college, I decided to work on a PhD dissertation project that centered on DNA repair. I'd be studying the details of the processes by which cells fix DNA lesions, processes without which none of us would be alive.

It was easy to explain DNA repair when my friends and family members asked me what I did in the lab. We're all familiar with the danger of DNA damage. For instance, we're regularly warned of the dangers of UV radiation, and we've been taught to use sunscreen to protect our skin from the cancers that UV radiation-induced breakages could eventually cause. We all know to avoid cigarette smoke, preventing its carcinogenic components from damaging our DNA molecules.

Cells are equipped with sophisticated tools that combat DNA damage. Several cooperating groups of cellular molecules function in specific, well-regulated ways in order to repair damaged DNA (Lodish 2004). Most of these molecules are proteins, and they continuously collaborate with one another to search for lesions, assess the severity of the damage and repair it. At the beginning of my graduate school research, I imagined DNA repair molecules to be grand cellular saviors. DNA repair, to me, seemed to be a biological metaphor for redemption. These enzymes had one end goal: make it as though the DNA damage never even occurred in the first place. It was the same end goal as that of my personal redemption. These biological systems cooperated to correct the root of the problem. Our health seems to require molecular flawlessness, and when our cells fall short of perfection, amends must be made.

Unsurprisingly, I discovered over the course of my study that the reality of DNA repair is far more nuanced than it seemed when I started grad school. While cells have many tools at their disposal for correcting DNA damage, correction is only one type of tool they use. There's an alternative approach to repairing DNA lesions that doesn't include correction. It's called lesion bypass (Lehman 2007) and in this mode of repair, lesions are maintained within the genetic code, uncorrected. Instead of repairing them, the cell calls into action a specialized group of enzymes that treat the area of the lesion with extra care.

DNA lesion bypass often occurs when the cell identifies a lesion while actively synthesizing new DNA. This process of copying the DNA is critical; the new copy must be correctly copied and fully intact when it is passed to a newly forming daughter cell. This function is so important and so foundational to the health of the new daughter cell, that the cell is equipped to continue making the copy, even when a lesion is encountered. To halt the process at the site of the lesion would introduce risk. The molecules that copy the DNA would easily lose their place and risk copying a region multiple times, or leaving a region uncopied. It's better for the apparatus to keep going, finishing the task at hand, even when that task is being accomplished with flawed materials. There is a complex network of molecular signals that ensures that the most prudent path will be taken.

How is it that a cell keeps going, even in the presence of tremendous damage? Cells need to proliferate in order to ensure the continued viability of the organism, but if the damage in a DNA molecule is proliferated, the health of the entire system is jeopardized. The cell overcomes this challenge by calling into action a specialized set of molecules when it copies the damaged region. These molecules differ from the regular ones in a few important ways: they're faster, less accurate, less specific and less selective. They are error-prone. Lesion bypass molecules produce imperfect but functional mRNA transcripts that go on to produce imperfect but close-enough approximations of these cells' protein products. The system isn't perfect, and neither are its products. The imperfect products, however, are good enough to allow the cell to continue living and growing.

Lesion bypass molecules are imperfect, and it's precisely because of this imperfection that they're able to continue replicating DNA past the lesions. Normal DNA-copying molecules are highly accurate, and their proofreading domains usually do not permit them to continue replicating across a lesion. The error-prone molecules are the only ones that can continue across an area of damage. They regularly introduce errors, and because of this, they introduce a small amount of diversity to the genomes of daughter cells. Because of this diversity, even though the offspring DNA is imperfect, its imperfections will be different from those of its parent. There's strength in this diversity. The weaknesses of one cell are distinct from the weaknesses of its slightly genetically distinct neighbor. An organism whose cells have idiosyncratic imperfections is more resilient than one whose cells' imperfections are uniform. The error-prone nature of lesion bypass molecules are the qualities that allow life to persist, even in the face of damaging attacks and potentially disease-causing pitfalls. Surprisingly, imperfection promotes health and gives life.

As a young adult I tried to make such a high priority of overcoming my imperfections, which I believed to be my inherent sinful nature, that I neglected the work of truly caring for myself. The lesion bypass pathway illustrates a wholly different way to respond to imperfections. It's an image of adaptation: the cell's tools accommodate its own weaknesses, without correcting or fixing its own flaws. This approach allows for the continued healthy function of the system. Lesion bypass shows us that there are times when the root problem need not be addressed, but instead what's needed is flexibility. The cell needs to find a way to function that accommodates the problems, flaws and errors it contains. This adaptation, in some cases, is the only path toward continued growth and life.

The type of DNA repair that I intuitively imagined as a young graduate student is simply not a viable possibility in all situations. When the cell has the resources and machinery available to fix a lesion outright, then it does so. When the cell encounters damage while in the midst of performing its essential functions, error-prone lesion bypass molecules are its saving grace. These molecules provide a path forward despite the presence of flaws, and they are capable of providing this path because of their imperfect, error-prone nature. The lesion bypass pathway subverts the notion that complete genomic integrity is necessary for a cell to be healthy. Some flaws can be tolerated, and in order to tolerate their own flaws, the cell must call specialized enzymes into action, ones that have enough of a propensity to break the rules that they can handle imperfections. The continued life and growth of a cell are prioritized above the pursuit of complete genomic perfection. The cell is doing far more important things than becoming perfect.

DNA lesions do not solely arise from external foreign agents. As by-products of their normal reactions, cells produce DNA-damaging toxins of their own. Under normal, healthy conditions, DNA molecules are in constant danger, surrounded by toxins that are produced by the cell they in-habit. The damage-inducing danger is internal, natural and normal, and the damage is correspondingly pervasive: a DNA molecule in a single cell is estimated to experience an average of 1 million breakages per day. Flaws cannot be seen as aberrations, but are clearly normal in cellular life.

DNA lesion repair, with all of its multifaceted catego-ries and aspects, actually moves toward a different end goal than what I initially imagined. Flawlessness, purity and perfection are not the goals of the cell's repair mechanisms. The damage only needs to be addressed to an extent that allows the whole system to continue living and growing.

Every time I was reminded of my sinful nature when I was a striving young evangelical, I felt defeated. I knew that selfish behaviors had the power to derail me, and my ina-bility to overcome these behaviors left me disillusioned and hopeless. The biological paradigm is strikingly different from the model to which I aspired, though. Cells are simply not equipped to pursue perfection, but they still achieve health and proper function with astonishing regularity. They're remarkably well-equipped with resilience, the abil-ity to remain functional despite imperfections.

What if I applied this paradigm to my own treatment of my personal flaws, errors and struggles? Some flaws can be corrected outright. There are damaging behaviors and thought patterns that I can directly address and avoid. There are personal struggles, though that could only be ad-dressed and corrected if I halted my personal growth, dis-tracting myself from my important roles and relationships. In my pursuit of selflessness and self-control, I reached a point at which my efforts began to backfire. I was convinced that this was a quest for wholeness and growth, but instead I became paralyzed, so afraid of my own shortcomings that I was unable to move forward.

This cellular pathway by which damage is not corrected, but instead is accommodated provides a fresh metaphor. It's a subversive pattern and I seek to use it to search for the tools to accommodate my own shortcomings. It's a self-loving and self-compassionate approach in which I use every tool at my disposal in order to remain sensitive to my own weaknesses and creative in developing solutions. It's an approach that keeps the end goal always in view: the goal of function. I have more important things to do with my life than to futilely attempt to overcome my own nature. I have relationships to build, work to accomplish and beauty to experience.

Knowing when to accommodate my flaws and when to repair them is a matter of discernment. It requires sensitivity and an ability to clearly see my own weaknesses without becoming blinded by shame and self-condemnation. It requires creativity more than it requires perfection. This discernment is a form of wisdom that grows with time, and I believe it is available to each of us who are willing to give ourselves enough grace to reframe our own imperfections.

8

GOD'S PLAN

My skin was hot under the stage lights. The beams were blinding, and all I could see was the front of the sanctuary where I stood. I waited my turn, standing and inching my way forward, and now I was next in line.

Even without the heat from the lights, I still would have been sweaty from nervousness. My mind was going in a million directions at once, my thoughts a cocktail of excitement, anticipation and nervousness. I couldn't believe it was almost my turn. I'd only received one prophecy before in my life, but I was a little girl then. Thinking back to that time, it seemed I couldn't have possibly understood how important those prophetic words were. Everything felt different now. I was 14 years old and I felt ready. I wanted nothing more than to know God's plan for my life and I was certain that when I would receive those words, I'd know what to do with them.

I was only a few feet away from the Prophet now. He was a traveling minister, known in our loose network of churches for his ability to prophesy. We believed that these prophecies were prayers over individual people that delivered to them God's specific and personal instructions, declarations or warnings. We believed that this traveling Prophet was the mouthpiece of God and on the basis of his reputation and track record alone, we trusted him as a spiritual authority. The Pastors of our church hired him to spend the week with our congregation, preaching sermons and praying for us one-by-one, administering personalized prophecies to as many of us if were willing to receive them.

I furrowed my brow, squeezed my eyes shut, and clasped my hands in front of my body. Something monumental was about to happen, so I tried as hard as I could to prepare myself. I looked like I was praying and I was in fact mumbling sounds and syllables — my best approximation of speaking in tongues. I had heard my fellow church members speak in tongues my entire life, an ability I'd been taught was a special gift from God, a prayer language given as a gift to faithful, committed Christians. I faked my own prayer language for years, in an effort to avoid the embarrassment of being exposed as one who was actually unworthy to receive the gift of a prayer language. My fake prayer language was convenient in times like this when I couldn't focus enough to actually pray coherent prayers. My mind was racing, imagining what the Prophet's words would be, what he'd predict and what he'd say about my future. The Prophet was about to reveal God's plan for my life.

This was the last night of the year's Prophetic Meetings. Sunday morning church services were a regular part of life for us, but during the week of the Prophetic Meetings, we didn't just go to church on Sundays. We also had services every evening for three nights in a row. At each Prophetic Meeting, we were at church for hours, long past our usual bedtimes, singing, dancing, jumping up and down in the aisles, praying, shouting, celebrating and repenting. Every service started with worship songs, and the songs the worship band played for the Prophetic Meetings were the loudest, fastest, most drum-heavy songs in the repertoire. The church members flooded the aisles, leaving our seats in order to have plenty of space to dance, jump, twirl, clap and kick along to the music. The sanctuary lights were dimmed during worship in order to decrease our inhibitions. This was a time for expressive, exuberant celebration.

Once the music ended, when sweat was dripping down every face and every pair of calves was burning from the previous 20 minutes of constant motion, we all filed back to our seats. The stage lights came on, illuminating the pulpit, which was at the front and center of the stage, which was soon occupied by the spirit-filled Prophet. Even now that we were seated and listening to a sermon, the energy in the room remained high. The preaching at Prophetic Meetings was always the loudest we heard all year. The sermon's content ranged from rebuke to joyful celebration, but throughout every tonal transition, the volume remained maximal. Callbacks spontaneously erupted across the sanctuary, congregation members yelling out: "Amen!" "Yes!" and "Thank you Jesus!" The Prophet, looking out through the glare of the stage lights as he paced back and forth behind the pulpit, acknowledged every outburst, welcoming the energy and affirmation.

As the end of the sermon neared each night, my attention heightened and my pulse quickened. The best part was about to start: prophetic ministry. The Prophet's invitation was slightly different each night. Some nights, all who were looking for "more of Jesus" were invited up front, and nearly the entire congregation would form a line, waiting for the Prophet to pray, speaking in tongues and laying his hands on us until the Holy Spirit gave him a personal prophecy to deliver. Other nights, those who were "struggling to find Jesus" were invited, and the line would be much shorter—only those willing to admit to a struggle would make their way up front. Tonight, the call went out to all those "searching for God's plan" for their lives. "*This is my night*," I thought. I'd turned 14 two months earlier, and in this phase of adolescence, I was newly concerned with "figuring out God's plan" for my life.

We believed in a God who had a detailed plan—a best case scenario life—for each of us and it was up to us to decipher those plans. We believed that even though humans make choices, God knows in advance which choices we will make. Even beyond that, we believed that our capacity to make choices and our propensity to choose certain options originated in God. Nothing could surprise our God. I believed that God's ideal plan for me included everything from a general life timeline to the specific details of my days. Prophecies, in our church, were personal hand-delivered revelations of God's plan for us. The Prophet's words would be pure godly wisdom.

As we neared the portion of the meeting that was dedicated to individual prophecies, I was sitting next to my parents in the center of the sanctuary. My flurrying thoughts calmed and my internal pep talk began. It was time to get over the butterflies in my stomach and the weakness in my legs and walk forward to receive my prophecy. *"You're the perfect age, at the perfect place in life, and anyway, this is the last night of Prophetic Meetings. If you don't go up now, you'll have to wait until next year for another chance."* I stood up, left my seat and shuffled past my mom and dad, making my way to the aisle.

My turn arrived. I felt the Prophet's warm, slightly damp palm press on my forehead. My eyes remained squeezed tightly shut, and I shuffled forward half a step. I felt a wave, a shock, a visceral sense of expectation. *"It's happening."*

Two hands pressed on my back and my shoulders. I glanced back and saw my parents standing behind me, both laying one hand on my back. My dad, standing behind my left shoulder, held out a cassette tape recorder between the Prophet's face and mine, ready to capture every word he said. I was relieved that my prophecy was being recorded. I believed the Prophet's words would be delivered straight from God, and it was comforting to know that I'd have a way to remind myself of everything he said.

The Prophet, with the palm of his right hand pressing on my forehead, placed his left hand on the back of my head, down low by my neck. His hands were huge and heavy, but I felt surrounded rather than crushed by their pressure.

He was speaking now but I recognized no words. He was speaking in tongues, his gibberish syllables following a tight rhythmic pattern. I fell into a rhythm of my own, faking my own prayer language, trying to let it flow effortlessly while focusing just enough to avoid repeating the same syllables too often. I was careful to always keep my voice quieter than his, finding a way to participate in the prayer without disrupting it. I fell silent as soon as I heard him speaking coherent English words.

"Your life is like a track. It's a train track and you're going along, you're right on track, and all you need to do is stay on that track."

A few tears were running down my face, and I heard sniffles from my parents behind me. This prophecy was peaceful and beautiful, and it was everything I dreamed of. All of my teenage anxieties started to fade from my mind. I felt a little less pressured to choose the right college, make the right relationship decisions and select the right career. This train track image was comforting and reassuring, and it was melting away the stress I felt when I thought about my future. As long as I simply stayed on my track, everything would work out.

The Prophet's palm pulled back a bit, no longer so heavy on my forehead. He stopped praying in tongues and shifted his stance. He was disengaging from his prayer, shifting his focus away from the spiritual realm and toward me standing in front of him in the crowded front of the sanctuary. My nose was red and puffy and my teary red eyes were squeezed shut. My face was wet with the most peaceful tears I'd ever cried. I opened my eyes and saw that his glasses were off and his eyes were hidden behind the back of his hand, slowly rubbing back and forth on his sweaty brow.

"When you're traveling along this train track, there will be times when you'll come to a split in the tracks and it will be that point where you need to make a decision. You'll ask yourself 'do I switch tracks or not?'"

I sensed tension and hesitation in his voice, but he was looking straight into my eyes. His delivery was dutiful, not nearly as joyful as it was a moment ago. It seemed he knew he had to say this part, but he wished he could skip it. My heart was racing. Why couldn't my prophecy have just ended a minute ago when my future seemed so peaceful and certain?

"The point is, when you come to these points of transition, go slowly. Don't...get...sidetracked. There is a fog in your future and you will get through it. You will be OK, but the Devil will try to confuse you and get you off track."

He was earnest. The slow trickle of tears was now a steady stream, having rapidly turned from peaceful to terrified tears.

The Prophet's tone lightened a bit. "You'll be OK! You just have to go slow. Be careful at those interchanges." Maybe he could read the look on my face, seeing how seriously I was taking this. His affirmation did little to ease my concern. I saw how earnest he was a moment ago, and I'd already made careful note of his reluctance.

My dad popped the cassette tape recorder open, took out the tape and placed it firmly in my hand. He was redeyed and sniffling too. I felt his pride and affirmation, even after the confusing and disappointing second half of my prophecy. I couldn't make eye contact though. I was too overwhelmed with emotion.

That cassette tape became my most prized possession. I took it home from the Prophetic Meeting that night, holding it carefully in my lap on top of my Bible and prayer journal as we drove home. Once we were home, I placed it on the bookshelf in my room right next to my Bible. To me, it was priceless. I listened to it over and over in the months and years that followed, memorizing the words the Prophet had spoken to me. I wrote the Prophet's words verbatim in my prayer journal, hoping that by seeing it written out in front of me, the prophecy might start to mean something new; something more hopeful.

On one hand, it was comforting to know that God had a train track for me. I liked the idea of a world free of chaos, and to me, these prophetic words confirmed that the details of my life weren't randomly occurring but that they had been specifically planned. Now, equipped with my prophecy, my only task was to stay on my track.

Contained as well within this very prophecy, though, was hopelessness: a recognition of the inevitable and dangerous fog coming my way. When I listened to the cassette tape recording of my prophecy, I couldn't avoid imagining the Prophet's face, seeing the fear that was in his eyes as he prophesied. During the first part of my prophecy, the part that foretold joy, direction and purpose, I was overwhelmed with gratitude for my God's omnipotence. During the final part of that prophecy, though, as I received a warning of the danger in my future, it was that very same attribute of God, his unthwartable omnipotence, that birthed a distinct hopelessness in me. If God's plan for me included "a fog," I wondered if there was actually anything I could do to prevent it from overtaking me.

What would happen if I got sidetracked? How would I know that I'd fallen prey to the fog and taken the wrong track at the interchange? What would be the signs? What if it wasn't intentional, but I got sidetracked because I just didn't pay enough attention? Would God give me some extra chances if I went the wrong way inadvertently? How would I know I was going "slow" enough at those interchanges?

I'd expected promises from this prophecy, but instead, God sent me a warning. God's plan for me included confusion and pain.

This was the first time I started to believe that God's plan for my future included difficulty. According to the Prophet, God had created a destiny for me, but that destiny was not solely one of prosperity and joy. My future included confusion. I could expect a future so precarious that God had to specifically warn me about it through this Prophet. I used to think that God's plan would make me feel secure, but now it just felt like a trap. Even more than that, it felt like a curse. Was there even any sense in trying to make wise choices? Maybe the fog would come my way regardless of my choices. The fog's danger was so great that God had been compelled to warn me about it. I couldn't imagine that I would have a chance of successfully overcoming it.

In my church, we only talked about the positive aspects of believing in a God who is in control of everything. We celebrated our personal relationships with the God who had planned every detail of our lives, from the impactful to the minor. I believed in a God who had a plan that included which jobs I'd apply for, which house I'd live in, who I would marry and when my future children would be born. I'd been taught that God's plan included even the minor, seemingly inconsequential details of my life: the type of car I'd drive, who my next-door neighbor would be and who would stand behind me in line at the coffee shop. I prayed prayers of gratitude for my heavenly safety net, and I prayed prayers of petition that my heavenly hedge of protection would guard me from evil. At church services, we sang songs of peace and contentment, relishing the generosity of our God who protected and cared for us all the days of our lives.

We never talked about the hopelessness that comes

along with believing in a God who is in control of every-thing. Now that I'd received my prophecy, the idea of a cha-otic world was starting to sound attractive, a preferable alternative to the certainty with which I expected to find confusion, disorientation and danger in my future.

Now, I was discovering the negative side of believing in an omnipotent God. A God who is in control of every-thing is a God who not only sends us blessings and saving grace, but who also sends us pain, doubt and loss. As long as God was sending me promises of prosperity, I could wholeheartedly celebrate God's omnipotence. When God delivered warnings of danger and pain, that very same om-nipotence felt confining and hopeless.

It was against this backdrop of my belief in an omnipo-tent, controlling and involved God that I first learned about genetics. I believed in a God who plans every detail of the human experience, and genetics seemed to uncover the de-tails of the way in which this control is executed. The cause-effect relationships between genes and traits appeared to exemplify God's providential control. While the train tracks and the fog were elements of God's plan that required a Prophet's illumination, biology seemed to teach me that there were also pieces of my destiny that required no proph-ecies. I learned that these destiny-dictating elements were held in my body, located inside my cells and encoded in my DNA molecules. I envisioned an individual's genetic code as the key to unlocking the mysteries of human experiences, ranging from specific, relatively inconsequential details to monumental, identity-forming traits. I filled the gaps in my preliminary understanding of genetics by assuming that everything about me could be traced to my genetic blueprint.

Some of the traits that were dictated by my genetics were more important than the others. In fact, they seemed to have a hierarchy of significance. Some of my genetic traits seemed inconsequential, arbitrary and unimportant, like my eye color or the shape of my toenails. Then there were others that seemed foundational, forming aspects of my identity. These identity-forming traits shaped my self-perception and dictated the way I interacted with my world. One particular trait of mine held tremendous importance, beyond comparison with any other traits of mine. This was the fact that I had been born a female.

I don't remember learning about the differences between boys and girls. Instead, the differences seemed to simply always be apparent to me. I was not even conscious of my own understanding of gender when I was a child or adolescent. Nonetheless, my beliefs and my conceptualized ideals were being formed all along. I was part of a social community that overwhelmingly and unquestioningly assumed that human beings exist in two distinct categories.

The fact I was born female—a trait that manifests in every DNA molecule of every cell in my body—had profound cultural implications throughout my entire childhood. Distinct gender roles were especially important aspects of our evangelical culture. I was a child born into evangelicalism, and because of this, I was part of the only group of evangelicals that had never been evangelized. I became a part of evangelicalism at birth, long before I had the capacity to understand the doctrines undergirding this culture. By the time I began learning the actual tenets of our faith, the cultural norms of evangelicalism had already formed my thought patterns, behaviors and self-perceptions.

When I first spoke the words to claim my belief in Jesus and to ask him to come into my heart, I was three years old.

Like any three-year-old, I lacked even an echo of the maturity required to experience a true religious conversion. Even then, however, my entire world was contained within evangelical culture. My family and my community, the people I learned to trust and respect, all belonged to this group, and my childhood was spent observing their behaviors, adopting their traits and merging into their particular lifestyle. This continued to happen even though I wasn't conscious of it. Without my realizing it, I adopted the traits and tendencies that I observed around me, never realizing the particularity of this expression of evangelical church culture.

Of all aspects of evangelical culture, the behaviors, traits and lifestyle of evangelical Christian femininity had a profound effect on me. The everyday manifestations of femininity became incorporated into my habits and thought patterns when I was a young child. It was long after this groundwork had been laid that I was told that my femininity was far from happenstance, but that it was part of God's plan for me.

I have a vivid memory of the first time I recognized my own reflection in a mirror. It was just moments after my mom finished giving me a new haircut. This wasn't just any typical haircut, but this was a haircut with bangs. These were my very first bangs, too, and I saw them there in the mirror, falling straight down over my forehead and coming to a sharp straight line above my eyebrows to frame my squinty smile. My smile got even bigger and squinty-er as soon as I saw those bangs. I was thrilled. They were identical to my sister's. That was the entire reason I had desperately wanted this haircut; if I had bangs, I'd be just like my sister. I'd be one of the girls.

I knew I was expected to make myself look like a girl. My feminine appearance was made most prominent on Sundays when I went to church. I wore a dress to church every Sunday. I wore white or pink pantyhose with my dress, white socks that had a ribbon of lace gathered around the cuffs and shiny black Mary Jane shoes. Every girl at church wore this female uniform and the boys had their own uniform too. They wore dress pants with a belt and a tucked-in buttoned shirt.

Even on the other days of the week, I dressed differently from boys. The distinguishing factors were a bit less pronounced, as I wore pants and T-shirts Monday through Saturday, just like the boys did. Still though, my clothes were different. Mine had significantly more pink and purple in them and less blue and red. My clothes were lacier and flowerier. Mine had gathers and bunches, flares and frills. Boys wore muted tones, and their clothes tended to have square corners and straight lines.

I learned concrete aesthetic meanings of 'feminine' and 'masculine' before I was even a kindergartener, as did most Americans of my generation. In my church, though, I was taught that these aesthetic expressions were not arbitrarily chosen. Feminine aesthetics were outgrowths of what we believed about our feminine nature. Our personalities, our preferences, our demeanors and our body language would ideally match the soft lines, ruffles and flowery patterns in our clothing.

For the women in my church, feminine aesthetics extended far beyond clothing. Our understanding of femininity certainly contained elements of the general American concept of femininity, but it had its own particularities as well. We carefully chose to emphasize and enhance the attributes of our bodies that we considered to be ideally feminine. Girls' bodies should be sleek and slender, I learned, and girls should monitor their food intake to make sure they stayed slim. I'd hear men joke about their weight, my dad and my uncles leaning back in their chairs after a holiday meal, slapping their bellies and laughing about how stuffed and fat they felt. I don't remember hearing a woman reflect on the food she ate with anything but remorse. When women commented on their appearances, there was rarely humor in their voices, but instead I sensed genuine disgust. Men, it seemed, wanted to be taller, stronger and bigger, but women solely wanted to shrink themselves.

"Never ask a woman what she weighs." This was the common-sense advice I'd often hear my dad half-jokingly give to my brothers. There was no need to give that advice to me. By six years old, I had learned to be ashamed of the soft parts of my body and to try to eat as slowly and sparingly as I could.

By the time I reached my preteen years, I was being taught a version of the importance of "finding my identity in Christ" that was tailored specifically to young women. I heard it in our church youth group girls' seminars. I read it in books written for evangelical Christian women. I was asked about it one-on-one by my small group leaders and accountability partners. I learned, by all of these avenues, that "finding my identity in Christ" could help me to accept the inadequacies of my body and the flaws in my appearance. It was meant to be a warning or a tip that would help me transcend body-related shame, but it came so early and it was repeated so frequently that it actually became its own source of body shame. It functioned as a self-fulfilling prophecy. Without being fully aware of it, I began to equate femininity with being ashamed of my body. Rather than subverting the notion that our bodies were inadequate, the Christian women's books I read and the women's seminars I attended gave me tools for accepting my own inadequacies. I was being prescribed a cure for a disease I didn't have. I eagerly accepted it though, and every time I prayed that God would help me to accept my body how it was, I unknowingly reinforced my own damaging belief that my body was unacceptable. I reinforced the notion that I was incapable of fully accepting my body unless I received divine intervention.

These ideals of feminine aesthetics were prominent on the surface, but femininity ran much deeper than the skin. Psalm 31:30, the verse that I wrote on an index card and kept on my bedroom mirror for years, was a frequent biblical reference used in our girls-only youth group lessons:

"Charm is deceitful and beauty is vain, but a woman who fears the Lord is to be praised."

'Fearing the Lord' is an abstract concept that is difficult to define in concrete terms. My church, however, for better or for worse, masterfully applied concrete meanings to abstract concepts. Behavioral patterns and physical aesthetics became conflated with God-given female identity. I noticed how most of the women and girls around me spoke, and it was different from the way men spoke. I heard a lilting inflection and a trailing off at the ends of phrases when women spoke, but men tended to use their voices in a louder, bolder way. I noticed the women around me laughing differently from men — gentle, soft and pretty, rarely boisterous or hearty. There was a particular style of dress worn by the women in my church, an embodiment of the very thin line that evangelical females were expected to walk. Attractiveness and prettiness were qualities of a woman fulfilling her biblically feminine role, but a sexually suggestive aesthetic was to be avoided at all costs. I could tell that it was important for me to be pretty without being alluring, feminine without being sexual and perpetually caring and compassionate without ever being too loud or pushy.

No one ever told me explicitly that I wasn't supposed to act or dress in a way that would be perceived as masculine. They didn't have to say it. As a very young girl, I had already begun to believe that my intrinsic femaleness should be accompanied by extrinsic elements. I could tell that if I rejected feminine aesthetics in favor of a traditionally masculine appearance, I would stand out, not as an innovator but as a defector.

Through my high school youth group years, I never really pushed back against the behavioral components of my assigned gender role. I watched, though, as a few others in my community pushed back, and it was clear that the church equated rejection of gender-assigned aesthetics with rejection of God's plan. Concern was expressed and interventions were made for those who didn't embrace the aesthetic associated with their assigned gender, and the concern stemmed from a genuine desire for a return to godliness. The strict adherence to these concrete definitions of gender expression was tremendously damaging. I saw firsthand that conflating godly living with appearance produced trauma, specifically for those who existed on the margins of my church's norms.

Puberty and the dawn of my youth group era ushered in an entirely new understanding of the doctrines underlying my own femininity. I was taught an additional narrative about God's plan for me as a woman. Now, it wasn't just my appearance and my behavior that were determined by my gender, but I was taught that God had a plan for my relationships as well, also formed by the fact I was female.

I was taught in youth group that I should make a "husband list," detailing the traits I hoped to find in my future mate. Any dating decisions would be carefully scrutinized in accordance with this list. I was taught that it was only once marriage was a viable practical option that I would be permitted to consider dating. Marriage, I was told, was the end goal of any dating relationship, the ultimate form of companionship. I was taught to aspire to marriage and to pray for my future husband regularly.

Every female-specific Christian book, seminar or conference I ever encountered assumed that women marry men and have children. Of course, I knew adult women who were single or who were not mothers, but judging from the content of every women's teaching I heard and every women's book I read, I concluded that these women were extremely rare exceptions to the norm. Marriage and motherhood were esteemed aspects of female identity in my church. Our hierarchical understanding of gender roles meant that husbands were in leadership over their wives. This belief meant that marriage was a defining and validating relationship for women in ways that it was not for men. There was a very specific inferiority complex that began to creep into my thoughts when I, as a young woman, adopted the belief that in order to conduct my own adult life, I required male leadership.

By the end of college, my understanding of God's plan for women could no longer account for my experiences. I'd accumulated too much evidence that contradicted my church's beliefs about gender roles. Fault lines began to develop in the foundation of my beliefs about my own feminine destiny. I had female professors who were strong and confident, who spoke with authority that I'd never before seen expressed by women. I had female classmates who were independent, who exercised agency over their own life choices. I started to realize that there's more than just one appropriate way to be female. In fact, I was learning, there are as many expressions of femininity as there are female humans in the world.

Despite biological realities beyond my control, I was discovering that I had the capacity to make my own choices. The women I met in the new non-evangelical world around me lived their lives in a free manner. They pursued their interests, the advancement of their careers and the exercise of their roles beyond family roles, simply because they chose to do so, not out of scorn for motherhood or marriage. What I saw around me was not the familiar image of women attempting to imitate their imagined ideal expression of femininity. Instead, I saw femininity through a kaleidoscope, and I witnessed a diverse array of feminine expression. I had been taught to seek an ideal, and to minimize the aspects of my personality that might disrupt this ideal. Every component of myself, I was taught, should be in the service of my pursuit of biblical womanhood. It took very little time in college, though, to see that variation, diversity and difference were actually beautiful, strengthening aspects of the real world. By embracing individual interests, strengths and particularities, the women I saw around me enhanced the beauty of our collective human expression in an irreplaceable way.

It was only then, when my image of feminine expression began to transform that I realized how rigid, specific and arbitrary my beliefs about gender had been. The kaleidoscope began to turn and I started to see that the image of biblical femininity — the one I'd been taught was ideal, the one I'd been encouraged to revere and pursue, was simply one of many. No single image of femininity was the ideal or true image, but each displayed an aspect of the feminine experience, each building upon the others and expanding the meaning of femininity. None was more valid than the others or more important than the others, but all of them, when taken together, formed an intricate and elaborate beauty that could never be portrayed by just one of these images alone.

In my college years, as my world was getting a little bigger and I was slowly learning the wisdom of withholding my judgment, I started to feel kind of disgusted by my old way of seeing things. The rigidity of my belief that there was only one ideal expression of femininity, and that it was my task to aspire to that ideal, had confined and burdened me in ways I didn't realize until that rigidity began to loosen. I gained a growing understanding of my capacity to make my own choices and of the beauty of diversity and difference. The idea of God-given gender destinies seemed as ridiculous as God-given roles for blue-eyed people as opposed to brown-eyed people. The concrete expressions of masculinity and femininity started to seem arbitrary to me. In fact, they started to seem imaginary. I wanted to believe that I had freedom, and that my destiny was self-made, not dictated by God, my circumstances or my genes. I felt more free and less constrained than ever, and I wanted to give myself full permission to build my own future, regardless of what I'd perceived to be God's plan.

Despite my new recognition of individual freedom, there was still a reality that I couldn't ignore that seemed to contradict the notion of individual agency. This was the component of human existence that seemed to dictate fates in an unthwartable manner. Human traits are undergirded by genetic realities. The concept of freedom was difficult for me to reconcile with the biological reality of genetic destiny. The goal of scientific investigation is often to identify cause-effect relationships, and as a young student of science, I learned to make the presupposition that nature, while complex, is undergirded by logical patterns.

This model left little room in my mind for the impact of human choice. The science of genetics seemed to seek full recipes for human beings. I learned that those recipes, the entirety of a person's genes, included instructions for creating even those human traits that not only manifest themselves physically, but also psychologically and socially. Included in this long list of human traits, of course, is the genetic recipe for gender.

Gender is determined by genes. It seemed disappointingly simplistic when I learned that gender is, in fact, determined by one gene: SRY, the sex-determining region on the Y chromosome. SRY unilaterally dictates whether a person is male or female. I understood that genes are not monolithic, but that metastable epialleles introduce ambiguity to a gene's product and horizontal gene transfer creates fluidity in a person's genetic code. Despite the multifaceted nature of gene interpretation, though, it's undeniable that there is a foundational biological reality associated with gender. Every cell in my body, I learned, is imprinted with femaleness and sends female-specific signals to the other cells in my body. Individual freedom was beginning to seem less and less real, now that I knew the true power of genes to determine and predict biological realities. My biology seemed to dictate my traits in a way that was hauntingly similar to the divine destiny I'd learned about in my childhood.

In order to perceive biology as predictive and deterministic, I had to view biological gender as a binary quality dictated unilaterally by anatomical sex. In reality, the actual manifestation of biological gender is remarkably more complex than this simplistic definition allows. The manifestations of biological gender are multiple and multifaceted. None of these manifestations are described by distinct categories, but each exists over a broad range of possibilities.

The most obvious manifestation — and the basis for gender assignment in our society — is anatomical sex, characterized by external sex organs. Anatomical sex is further characterized by internal sex organs, and even further by secondary sex characteristics. Secondary sex characteristics are those traits that are not necessary for reproduction, but that are linked in some way with sex. For males, these traits include facial hair growth, vocal deepening and Adam's apple enlargement. For females, these traits include enlargement of the breasts, widening of the hips and narrowing of the waist. None of these traits are concretely binary. Males don't all have the same tone of voice, and it's easy to identify examples of females whose voices are deeper in tone than males' voices. Gender-specific traits manifest over broad spectra.

The origins of biological gender exemplify the nuance at the foundation of gender determination. Every embryo begins its life with the potential to become both male and female. During the first few weeks of development, the embryo is poised, ready to develop whichever sex characteristics its hormone signals dictate. Two distinct precursors of sex organs begin to form: one tiny duct that could develop into male genitalia and another that could develop into female genitalia. Genital development doesn't begin until about 10 weeks after embryogenesis. A cascade of molecular signals is triggered by genetic factors and results in physical manifestations. It is this cascade that directs the development of sex-specific organs.

A cascade is wild and unpredictable. The path taken by a drop of water descending from the precipice of a waterfall is not a straight line. It's not a single pre-determined path. Each drop that falls creates its own path, propelled from the watershed, colliding with its neighbors and crashing into its surroundings until it reaches its destination in the pool below. Genetic determination of sex is like the precipice of a waterfall. It's the watershed of a cascade. Genetic sex is embedded in the genome at embryogenesis, written into a pair of sex chromosomes, one inherited from the father and one from the mother and it is sealed for life, unchanged in healthy embryos. Females have two "X" sex chromosome and males have an "X" and a "Y" sex chromosome. The SRY gene is the single determining factor, located on the Y chromosome, and thus present in males but not females. This gene, however doesn't directly signal the growth of male genitals. Instead, there is a long succession of intermediate steps between inheritance of a Y chromosome and growth of a penis and testicles.

SRY produces the protein TDF (testis-determining factor), which, as the name describes, directs development of the testes (Berta 1990). The testes function in two ways, and there are two distinct types of testis cells that respectively execute these functions: sertoli cells and leydig cells. Sertoli cells are responsible for blocking the development of female genitals and leydig cells are responsible for producing testosterone, the hormone that promotes development of male genitals.

Female embryos, whose genomes lack the SRY gene, do not produce a high abundance of testosterone and, in the absence of the male hormone, the tiny duct that is the precursor to male genitalia simply degrades on its own. From this point forward, the female journey from genes to biological manifestation of gender proceeds in a stepwise, cascading fashion, similar to the process in males.

Leydig cells foster male genital development by producing testosterone. It's important to recognize, though, that testosterone does not direct the development of male genitalia, but only directs the development of internal genital structures, like the epididymis, seminal vesicles, ejaculatory duct and ductus deferens. In order to develop external organs, a chemical reaction must first take place: conversion of testosterone to a modified form called DHT, a process that is facilitated by an enzyme.

When I learned these details of the manifestation of biological sex, I began to discover just how much ground is covered between inheritance of genetic sex and physical manifestation of sex. Not only this, but these steps do not progress predictably from one to the next, but each is modulated by the outcomes of the previous steps, along with myriad environmental and contextual forces. The exact ratio of leydig cells to sertoli cells varies among embryos. The amount of TDF protein expressed from the SRY gene during those first 10 weeks of an embryo's development will vary, influenced by a multitude of interdependent epigenetic factors. The available amount of the enzyme that converts testosterone to DHT will vary from person to person. Each aspect of the processes undergirding the manifestation of gender is so complex, organic and interdependent that dramatic variation, even between individuals who express the same genetic sex, is completely reasonable and expected.

When I learned these details, it became clear that genes, which I was inclined to regard as monolithic identity-determining factors, are much less powerful than I initially thought. Genes are just molecules, and they exist in varying abundances and possess varying activities within various contexts. Their possible functions can be characterized precisely, but their actual functions are profoundly influenced by their surroundings. Claire Ainsworth, in a 2015 *Nature* article, analyzed and synthesized recent research findings regarding sex-related genes. She discussed *WNT4* and *RSP01*, two gender-related genes, neither of which are capable of determining gender, but both of which direct the development of female sex characteristics. The products of these genes vary in activity and abundance among individuals. She comments on what we observe in humans and other animals, calling it a "complex process of sex determination, in which the identity of the gonad emerges from a contest between two opposing networks of gene activity." Freedom and fate are complementary aspects of our biology and they work with each other, together creating our biological identities.

The SRY gene is not a blueprint, a precise predictor or even an instruction manual. In reality, it is no more than a starting point. SRY sets in motion the unfolding, evolving, cascading journey between the genetic basis of gender and the emergence of gender-related traits. SRY signals to other molecules, which signal to other genes, which are also receiving signals from chemicals in their surroundings, which trigger production of hormones, which signal to other genes in other cells. As the cascade proceeds, SRY becomes further and further removed from the cell's molecular events. SRY becomes less and less involved in determining gender-related traits. Despite this, that gene is still an essential starting point. SRY is the first signal that sets the cascade in motion, and no gender-related traits would ever develop without it.

When I received my prophecy, I believed fervently in a God who could speak to me through a Prophet and I couldn't imagine that God's plan was anything other than a detailed blueprint for my guaranteed future. Genetics shows me another possibility. The inherent elements, the pieces that we assume to be precisely predictive and in direct correspondence with outcomes — those pieces are only involved in the first step. From there on, the system enters a complex landscape of action, reaction and interaction of environmental and internal signals. What if I see my own life through the lens of this biology, considering freedom and fate to be partners rather than opposites? While the complex landscape of cellular life includes the interactions of genes, hormones, chemicals and molecules, our human experience emerges out of our intrinsic traits, our cultural traditions and norms, our education, our understanding of our history and much more.

What the SRY gene illustrates is that order and freedom,

the two forces which I had been taught to believe were mutually exclusive, are actually dance partners. They cannot be disentangled. Yes, each person is born with intrinsic elements. The presence of SRY in the genome is indeed unambiguous, and its presence is necessary for the development of male-associated sex characteristics. This gene, however is not a blueprint. It's simply the first line of the instruction manual. It's not SRY itself that manifests biological gender characteristics, but the way that this natural element interacts with its surroundings is what creates reality.

The intrinsic element — in this case, SRY — is like a watershed. It determines which side of the mountain the rainfall will traverse, but after this initial decision, it has no further influence. The context, surroundings and environment take over from there. The cascade is so complex and variable, as each drop and each tiny stream is channeled, pushed, crushed and guided by every other drop and tiny stream, that the specific details of the path are unpredictable. Even within the confines of nature, there is true freedom. Destiny only makes the first decision. Freedom governs the rest of the process, and the possibilities truly do seem to be infinite.

When I imagine this biological image as a metaphor for my own life, I begin to see my own story differently. I'm able to tell a narrative about my life that involves more freedom. This teaches me that I can simultaneously embrace my freedom and honor the inherent elements of my identity. Both freedom and destiny are aspects of my human experience, and both are shaping my reality.

I no longer hold the fervent belief that I held when I was 14, my belief in a God who speaks directly to us through Prophets. I don't know if there is any sort of God who intervenes and speaks with humans in such a way, and I don't know how I would determine who that God's Prophets were, even if I did believe in that God's existence. I do know, however, that the way I frame my life deeply matters.

There's a story that I tell myself about myself, a set of beliefs that I hold about my capacity to make choices, about my freedom and my opportunities. This story becomes the core of what I believe about myself and it defines what's possible for me. I now consider my prophecy, complete with its image of foggy train tracks to be one such story. I no longer believe that this prophecy ever had the power to dictate my future, and treating it as an unthwartable destiny brought me nothing but anxiety. The words of the Prophet have become powerful in an altogether new way, however, as I've learned to see them not as an omen of my inevitable destiny but as a way to frame my life. In retrospect, there's no better way to describe my experience of wrestling with my faith over the past decade than as traveling through a fog. As I learned to look through the figurative kaleidoscope, began to challenge my own understanding of God, and recognized the particularity of the ideals I'd espoused, I felt as though I was passing through a thick, heavy cloud. Confusion and anxiety came first, long before any glimmer of freedom and hope broke through that thick fog. It was disorienting in ways I couldn't have imagined as a 14-year-old fervent believer. The words of that Prophet, though I now question his motivation, inspiration and mental condition, still echo in my mind. Those words equip me with a way to react when I encounter the fog of confusion: continuing on, following my course with care and sensitivity. The details of the particular train track I will follow and the particular fog that I will navigate will be determined by my experiences, shaped by the intricate concert of interacting forces in my context. It's a complex system that, from my vantage point, looks a lot like freedom.

I believed that God had a detailed, unthwartable destiny planned for me, and I believed that the certainty of that destiny left no room for individual freedom. This concept was comforting only when I expected my destiny to be full of prosperity, peace and joy. Once I began believing that my destiny included confusion, disorientation and pain, I slowly started to resent the all-powerful God who had determined that destiny. I thought that believing in complete personal freedom would cause me to become disoriented, but I was becoming disillusioned by the notion of a God who controls everything. For me, neither lens could fully encompass my lived experience, nor was either of these lenses palatable.

Biology illustrates the complex reality of our lives: both freedom and destiny simultaneously create our lived experience. The implication of this complexity is that both of these lenses can be used to frame our experiences, and reality exists somewhere between freedom and destiny. This means that when I start to feel the confinement of destiny, I can remind myself of the loose cascading processes triggered by my inherent capacities. I remember how freely a waterfall cascades from a watershed, and that my destiny is like that watershed, providing a starting point, but incapable of dictating every step toward the outcome. Another implication of this complexity is that when I feel paralyzed by the disorientation of chaos, and overwhelmed by the pressure of individual choice, I can remind myself of my individuality and my particular strengths and proclivities. There's a sense of meaning and purpose that I find in my inherent sense of self, and in my freedom to make choices.

Freedom and destiny are two views of the same world. They are two patterns viewed through the same kaleidoscope. Both of these images show us reality, but neither is a complete representation of reality on its own. With every turn of the kaleidoscope, as we watch the exact same pieces of confetti transform from one pattern to another, our understanding of reality becomes enriched.

Destiny writes the first line of each of our stories. Our intrinsic elements, the ones that make us unique, are real and powerful. They can give us a sense of meaning and purpose. But that first line is the only part of our story that destiny is capable of writing. Beyond that, the story can go in infinite directions. Each of us has the freedom to fill the page as we choose.

9

NEW LIFE

You never forget your first coffin. It's been 18 years, but I can still remember how it felt. Smoke machines surrounded the judgment throne of God where I lay motionless inside the black plywood box, playing the role of a departed soul who was awakening in the afterlife. Thick chemical smoke poured out of the smoke machine, flooding the room. I felt the smoke settling on my skin, forming a thin layer between me and the outside world. I kept tasting and smelling that smoke for at least a full day after each performance. Each night, once my family arrived back home, I stood in the shower until my fingertips looked like little pink prunes. The makeup, the sweat, the dirt and the smoke machine dust all had to be washed away. Every muscle in my body was sore from fighting against my demonic escorts and struggling against my chains and shackles in hell. I adjusted the water temperature until it was as hot as I could bear and I stood under the shower until I could no longer detect that distinct chemical smell of the fake smoke. I scrubbed my face, neck and hands until I could feel my plain, uncoated skin again, no longer masked by the heavy layer of white makeup, applied to make me look like a corpse. I scrubbed my scalp until the layer of fine, soft smoke machine dust was gone.

The bottom of the coffin was lined with rough black indoor/outdoor carpeting that felt like the rough side of Velcro. The tiny stiff fibers pushed against the polyester fabric of my funeral dress, subtly poking my back as I lay motionless. The soft plywood that had been used to build the coffin had been spray-painted black, and was not nearly as sturdy as it looked from the audience's point of view. I knew I couldn't lean against the sides of the coffin, or else they would bend and bow. There were a few splintering spots on the edges of the coffin and I knew their exact locations. I planned my movements precisely to avoid snagging my dress on the coffin. My muscle memory stored the exact height of the coffin's sides, and amidst the chaos following God slamming the Book of Life, I'd make sure to lift my leg high enough to avoid hitting the side. The sounds, the smells and the feelings of that coffin are still viscerally familiar to me.

My haunted house performance became a ritual. I repeated the motions, the expressions, the lines and the emotions over and over each night, then went back the next night and the next and did all of it over again. I lost track of time on performance nights, the ritual becoming second nature. I could access that sense of desperation, fear and horror with increasing ease. I earnestly believed that I would be judged by God in the afterlife, and that Hell was a literal place where God could send me if he chose. My performances were more than make-believe and hell was not just imaginary. In this repeated ritual, I embodied terror and shame. Panic and fear took up residence in my heart and mind, creating a vivid and visceral experience of my own possible eternal damnation.

I heard about death a lot at church. As a way of declaring our need for God, we sang songs about the brevity of our human existence. We sat in the sanctuary and listened to our pastor's sermons, which always included admonishments to live pure and holy lives in preparation for our eventual judgment before the throne of God. Reminders of human mortality were our favorite ways of beginning evangelistic conversations. Sermons usually ended with an altar call that encouraged the congregation to make their life decisions in light of the fact that they would one day die and, we believed, be judged by God in the afterlife. My youth group met on weekend afternoons to split into groups of three or four and walk through the church neighborhood, knocking on doors and asking residents unsolicited and jarring questions about their own mortality.

"If you were to die tonight, do you know where you would spend eternity?"

We believed that if we could fully accept the precarious nature of human existence, we would trust God more fully.

We believed, though, that life and death did not fully encompass the human story. Our focus on death was always paired with a celebration of our eventual ascension to heavenly glory. I was never quite as excited for this heavenly glory as others in my church seemed to be. My memory of the judgment throne of God, which I only saw from the perspective of a desperate and powerless damned soul, loomed too large in my mind for any heavenly anticipation to feel real. Even so, I sang with my congregation about the glorious day when we would all see the face of God. I prayed that God would keep me on the straight and narrow by reminding me of my heavenly reward. To me, it was clear that my earthly life should not be my focus, so I did my best to remind myself of my own mortality, learning to think of myself as a vapor, temporary and fleeting.

It wasn't just human finitude that we kept in the forefront of our minds. We believed it was important to remember that everything on earth is temporary: our cities and homes, even our rivers, forests and atmosphere. We believed that to focus too heavily on the earth and on earthly existence would distract us from what should remain our greatest concern. We wanted to direct our effort toward living pure and holy lives in service to God.

We hoped to accept our impermanence, and in this acceptance to avoid becoming heartbroken by the degeneration of our planet and of our bodies. We told ourselves there was nothing in the world that was even worth our heartbreak. We believed that the world was fallen, and that death, destruction and degeneration were natural symptoms of sin in the world. We believed humans to be, at our core, evil and incapable of good thoughts, desires or behaviors. Only the intervention of God, we believed, could cause us to be kind, generous or good. We believed that hardships, pain and suffering were natural outcomes of the unchecked evil of humanity. Ever-expanding landfills and graveyards were, to us, simply reflections of reality: human depravity and degeneration are continuously increasing. This perspective did provide me with an odd sense of comfort. It was reassuring to have an explanation for the pain I felt and observed in life, and for the disorientation that came when I thought about my eventual death. Still, more than anything else, my belief in my own fundamental sinfulness and brokenness brought shame and self-blame.

Hell was not the final scene in my church's evangelistic haunted house. The spooked audience members stood in the strobe-lit dungeon for a few deafening minutes, watching soot-smeared damned souls struggle against their chains and beat against the bars of their cages. The grim reaper tour guide waited a few minutes until he was sure that the tortured souls had effectively communicated their agony, then he ushered the audience out into the pitch-black hallway. As soon as the door of hell slammed behind the last audience member, my fighting, flailing body went limp, exhausted from struggling against the handcuffs around my wrists, and against the chains tethering me to the stage. I slumped back against the stage and Satan congratulated me on my convincing performance. I thanked him quickly while I unlatched my own handcuffs and slipped my feet out of the chains. I had no time to waste. Another tour group was already on its way, about to join us in hell at any minute. Their coffin girl, one of the other actors, another coffin girl who alternated performances with me each night, was already making her way to hell through the secret passageway.

After the original tour group moved far enough down the hallway that they were out of earshot, I jogged back to the judgment throne room, climbed inside the coffin again and allowed a collaborative group of angels and demons to close the lid, giving me just enough time to slow my breathing in preparation for the next tour group.

Still following the grim reaper down the dark hallway, the tour group rounded the first corner in the hallway outside of hell. Their ear drums were still ringing after the barrage of tortured screams and blaring death metal. A single bright white lightbulb turned on suddenly, and reflected off of the mylar-coated walls of the hallway. After several painful and disoriented seconds of blinking and squinting, the audience members' eyes adjusted to the brightness and the tour group saw a blonde-haired woman standing at the top of the staircase, glitter-enshrouded and clothed in shiny white robes. The silver feathery wings strapped to her back and the sparkling pale white hue of her skin, slathered thick with costume makeup, were the only clues the audience needed. She was an angel. The grim reaper was now cowering in the corner of the stairwell, and the angel rebuked him and dismissed him back to his home in hell. She was now the guide of this tour.

The angel invited the audience to follow her and they watched her silver -feathered wings flop and flap as she led them into a counseling room. A smiling man wearing khakis and a button-down shirt greeted them, and the angel entrusted the tour group to him. The man in khakis was the first person the tour group encountered who wasn't in costume. He was there to summarize the evangelistic message of the haunted house. He gave the audience specific instructions for avoiding the fate of the coffin girl. All they had to do was "confess with their mouth that Jesus is Lord and believe in their heart that God raised him from the dead" (Romans 10:9). Jesus died to pay for our sins, he told the audience, and anyone who believes and confesses this can be certain they will go to heaven when they die.

This message was the reason we put on the evangelistic haunted house every year. This production was exhausting and taxing for our congregation, and none of the actors, makeup artists, counselors, set designers or sound and light technicians were compensated. Nearly every member of the church worked at the haunted house for the majority of every weekend in October. None of us asked to be compensated, though, because we believed that we were using our time in the most meaningful and significant manner. We were preaching the gospel. Our intention wasn't just to scare people, or even to simply remind them of their own mortality. The counselors told the audience members that the fear they felt was a gift. We intentionally created an environment in which the audience would feel visceral terror, because we believed that to be terrified of eternal damnation was a gift from God. Terror had the power to wake us up to our need for God before it was too late.

After hearing the man in khakis present this version of the gospel, each visitor walked one-by-one into a hallway and chose a door by which to exit the haunted house. They found three foreboding doors, and they were instructed to walk through the door corresponding to their expected eternal destination. One door was marked "Hell," and we expected visitors to choose this door if they rejected our gospel message. The second door was marked "Heaven," and we expected it to be chosen by those who had already responded to the gospel, and knew for sure that their eternal destination was heaven. The third door was simply marked "?," and the button-down-and-khakis man explained to the visitors that on the other side of this door they would find counselors who could explain how to ensure admittance into heaven. Each visitor who chose this door would sit face-to-face with a church member and be instructed to pray, asking Jesus into their heart, becoming born-again and ensuring their place in heaven.

At the end of each performance night, we had a cast and crew debriefing meeting, and our pastor made an announcement, specifying the total number of "souls we saved." We believed our work had an eternal impact, and we celebrated that impact every single night. My bruised wrists and ankles, my sore throat, my costume makeup-induced skin irritation and my exhaustion all seemed worth it when I heard this tally of saved souls.

By the time I performed in the evangelistic haunted house, I'd already confessed belief in Jesus hundreds of times, repeating my confession over and over just to make sure it worked. My repeated confessions never quite silenced my doubts, though. I always questioned whether my salvation really was secure, and when I sinned, I wondered if that sin rendered my salvation null and void. I didn't just worry about the sins I could easily identify either, but I believed that my inherent sinful nature made it so that I probably wasn't even aware of all the ways in which I was sinning. My self-perception reflected the view of the psalmist, who wrote in reference to humanity: "who can discern his errors? Declare me innocent from hidden faults" (Psalm 19:12). I believed that as a naturally sinful person, I was probably so deeply entangled in sinful behaviors that they had begun to seem natural to me. I didn't even know how to identify or repent of those second-nature sins, but I still anxiously wondered if they invalidated my ticket to heaven.

My task as a believer was to swim upstream, fighting against the current of sin that was pushing everything on earth toward destruction. I believed that heaven and hell would be the only afterlife possibilities, and that entry into heaven depended upon belief, an incredibly elusive mental state. As a result, daily living became a high wire balancing act. Simple daily activities like eating, spending money or interacting with strangers began to seem like expansive landmine-riddled fields, where destructive and over-whelming sin always lurked just below the surface. This sin-focused version of the gospel produced self-hatred, self-doubt and anxiety in me, all of which were heavy burdens to bear.

Although I struggled to trust it, my church's gospel message did center on redemption. The redemptive message, however, only had the power to redeem each individual believer and had no impact on the degenerating planet or the depraved whole of humanity. According to our doctrines and teachings, salvation was simply a personal escape hatch. Although we believed that Jesus' death atoned for our sins and made our eternal heavenly lives possible, our personal atonement changed nothing for our unbelieving neighbors and for our planet. We believed that in order to be saved, each person had to make their own personal decision to accept Jesus into their heart. Jesus could save individuals, but the fate of humanity and of the earth would always be destruction. We believed the destiny of all humans, apart from the intervention of God, would be eternal torment in hell. The best we could hope for — the miraculous amazing grace for which we thanked God every day — was the loophole that Jesus had created when he gave each of us the opportunity to take our own personal escape route away from the natural destination of humanity: hell.

Any sense of heavenly hope that I had was tainted by my belief that every other person who hadn't accepted Jesus as their personal Lord and Savior would spend their eternity in hell. Maybe, I thought, I was God's one and only plan for saving someone. Maybe I was the only Christian that a particular acquaintance would ever know. If I failed to speak up and share the gospel, that person would be tortured in hell for all of eternity. I had gratitude for my own salvation, but it was dulled by my guilt over my own evangelistic shortcomings. I felt responsible for explaining to my friends and acquaintances how to ensure their admission into heaven, but I also felt overwhelmed by the task and deeply resentful of the God who burdened me with eternally impactful evangelistic duties.

Earthly life, to me, had no meaning of its own, but instead it was something to endure in order to have a shot at reaching my heavenly destination. I began to identify more and more with the biblical book of Ecclesiastes:

"What does man gain by all the toil
at which he toils under the sun?
A generation goes, and a generation comes,
but the earth remains forever." (Ecclesiastes 1:3-4)

I started to wonder why God created this degenerating world in the first place, and why God created humans to be sinful by nature. A God who would do all of this didn't seem to be a loving and gracious God. This was a villainous God who had intentionally burdened humanity with an impossible task.

There were moments when I could ignore the internal

dissonance that came from believing in this villainous God. I sang worship songs about heaven, I read, re-read, discussed and dissected rapture predictions, and listened to sermon after sermon, all interpreting the symbolic end-times language of the biblical book of Revelation. I felt that this was the only way I could continue to resist my sin and overcome the challenges of evangelism: reminding myself that one day I would be relieved of that pain.

I couldn't sing enough worship songs, listen to enough sermons or study enough scriptures, though, to ignore the dissonance forever. The God who would create sinners and then punish them for being exactly what he created them to be was not a God I wanted to continue worshipping. This realization was only possible when I began to accept that there could be a different conception of God. Slowly, I started to understand that "God" might not be a fixed concept, but in fact has been given wildly, beautifully diverse definitions across time and space. Thinking about God began to feel like looking through an infinitely turning kaleidoscope. I grew up believing that there was one and only one possible concept of God, and that it was fixed, constant and clearly definable. I started to see the beauty in accepting and embracing an image of a God who was not as retributive as the God I was taught to worship.

By the time I finished my PhD, I was finally able to articulate the impact of this transformation on my beliefs and thoughts. Biblical literalism no longer made sense to me and I could no longer stake my life's meaning on an eternal destination in a literal place called heaven. How could something as elusive as belief be such a significant litmus test, the factor that determined every person's eternal fate? How could I even know my own beliefs with any certainty? What would it actually mean to "believe in my heart that Jesus is Lord?" How would I know if I was believing fervently enough? Back when I believed that the Bible was literally true, my mortality was a lot more palatable. I believed that my death would not be my ultimate end, but that I would experience an afterlife, and that I could eventually find myself in heaven, plucked from the river of humanity that naturally flows into the fires of hell. Without that belief, I now believed that this earthly life was all I had. I couldn't rely on hope of heaven anymore, but I had to consider the possibility that this earthly life may be all there is.

In the world beyond my evangelical Christian community, while the topic of human mortality was generally avoided, I noticed that a lot of work was done to immortalize the dead. I found little comfort in this, though, because only a very select few of the dead could ever be effectively immortalized, and even their seeming immortality could only endure for a brief amount of time.

Granary Burial Ground in Boston, MA took me by surprise the first time I saw it. It's tucked tightly into a city block. Row after row of neatly organized gravestones stand inside, squeezed as close to one another as possible. Tiny as it is, as soon as I glanced inside, I knew it was not ordinary. Some of the gravestones in those rows were completely plain, bearing no inscriptions, and some were ornately engraved with detailed information about the deceased person's life. Dispersed all throughout the burial ground, towering over these tightly organized lines of stone slabs were monstrous monuments, rising up out of the earth. I could tell that these stones were making bold declarations of some kind. The stones bore long, elaborate and poetic descriptions, describing the influential, significant and history-making activities of the person whose remains were buried there. The importance of these dramatically memorialized individuals was certainly obvious; three people who signed the Declaration of Independence were buried there, as well as numerous other influential figures of colonial America.

These towering, imposing monuments were not what caught my attention, though. Surrounding them, lining the entire cemetery, were hundreds of other graves. These small gravestones formed tidy rows, tightly packed together. I recognized none of the names I read on those gravestones.

There were more graves than these too, and they were marked with nothing but a flat stone, an irregularly shaped rock, or a chipped, cracked piece of brick. Nothing about these gravestones, except the fact that they were located in a burial ground even indicated that they marked a grave. If there had once been any identifying information engraved on them, that information had long since eroded away. These blank, unremarkable bricks marked graves of real people who lived real lives. Each of these people once had an entire earthly experience of their own. They experienced their own childhood, adolescence and adulthood, with all the pain, joy and struggle of their particular experience of each phase. They built relationships, they worked hard, they created homes, they made a way for their families to survive. They beat the odds in unfriendly circumstances, survived enemy attacks, diseases, hunger and long winters. And now, just 300 years later, not even their names, their most basic identifying information, were remembered.

We like to think we're leaving a legacy, and we're quick to recognize those figures in history who did leave an observable legacy. It only takes a few minutes strolling through a cemetery, however, to realize how flimsy these legacies are. While the John Hancocks and Samuel Adamses of the world—the select few who appear in our history texts—are remembered as heroes, even their legacies are temporary, local and fleeting. The masses; the overwhelming majority of us never receive even this temporary memorialization, but are forgotten within a generation of our deaths.

Standing in Granary Burial Ground, it seemed clearer to me than ever before that my body, composed of the same chemicals that compose dirt, will eventually decompose, becoming dirt once again. Now lacking the theological certainty I had as a child and adolescent, I wasn't sure if there was anything meaningful in life beyond the material, concrete realm. From this mechanistic, materialist perspective, I started to see my life simply as a circuitous and convoluted pathway by which dirt in one location becomes dirt located somewhere else. It's not just us as individuals who will eventually die either, but it's the collective *us*. For instance, in 100 years, planet Earth will be populated by a completely new set of people, none of whom are alive now. Humanity undergoes a constant turnover. We each struggle, work, love, fight and pray, and yet it's hard to think of anything that endures beyond our lifetimes. Once I left behind my fundamentalism and biblical literalism, I no longer saw the universe as simply degenerating; I now saw its meaninglessness as well.

Thinking about death while still living is like watching a movie while sitting inches away from the screen. It's impossible to see anything clearly when you're that close to it. As a teenager terrified of hell and desperate to be spared from its flames and torture, I was too caught up in my own mortality to think about it clearly. Even in my most hopeful moments, when I was confidently anticipating heaven rather than anxiously fearing hell, I was preoccupied, focused on escaping my earthly life. My hope for heaven kept me disengaged with life. Regardless of whether my stance was fearful or hopeful at any given moment, I couldn't quite think about my own mortality without becoming caught up in it. It was an emotional, stressful, anxiety-infused concept and it always left me disoriented.

I found a way, though, to think dispassionately about

death, a way to back away from that movie screen so I could bring the full picture into my view. Humans are not the only mortals on earth, but we humans are made of components that are themselves mortal. Cells experience their own deaths, passing through the entirety of their life cycles within tiny fractions of our human lifetimes. When I think about cell death, I can think about it dispassionately, as an outside observer. Cell mortality doesn't shock me into the sense of existential fear and anxiety that human mortality does, and it leaves me free of emotional entanglements.

There's another layer still, a type of death that is even further removed from our human realm. Cells are not monoliths but are communities of their own, themselves composed of smaller components. Inside our cells are other individual entities, DNA and RNA molecules, protein chains and organelles. All of these pieces are continuously intertwining, interacting and reacting, modifying, promoting and suppressing one another in precise choreography. The members of cellular communities are engaged in a continuous cycle of creation and destruction. While these molecules are not classified as living, they generate and degenerate in a pattern that parallels the pattern of life and death. As humans, our mortality is layered. Our cells are the mortal components that make up our collectively mortal bodies, and these cells are themselves made out of mortal components.

Biologists can study the subcellular generation-degeneration cycle relatively easily. Cell components turn over so rapidly that we can track the entire process, without the limitation of observing only one isolated step at a time. On a subcellular level, we can observe degeneration as part of a much greater pattern. We can zoom out far enough to look for a through-line.

Cells are surprisingly hospitable, a quality we've already encountered in our exploration of cellular quiescence. Even unproductive cells are often supported as members of the whole. But of course, there are limits to this hospitality. There are times when a component of a cell is so broken, or when it malfunctions in such a damaging way that the cell must discard it. Sometimes the brokenness extends to the entire cell, and the whole thing self-destructs, ending its own life prematurely and abruptly. At other times, in situations where the brokenness is contained to just one component, the malfunctioning part is tagged and targeted by an elaborate waste removal system and is shuttled out of the cell.

The doomed cell components are usually targeted because they're disruptive. They're damaged so deeply and irreparably that they've gone rogue and they present a threat to the cellular community or to its environment. This targeted type of destruction can even be a defense mechanism against foreign invaders such as viruses. The cell can use this waste removal system to destroy invaders before they highjack the cellular machinery for their own purposes, which are typically destructive to the cell. There are also situations in which partial self-destruction is used as a means of cellular survival. When a cell is experiencing extreme stress or nutrient deprivation, it will off-load its non-essential components, destroying entire organelles in order to decrease its needs and increase its chances of survival.

As I first began learning about this natural pattern, it seemed that cells echo the story of degeneration and meaninglessness that I found in the greater scheme of the universe. It seemed to be one more image of the emptiness that was lamented throughout the book of Ecclesiastes. Cells and molecules, I found, break down over time, and they are temporary and transient, just as we humans are. Existence takes a toll, and it affects everything on earth, breaking things down and leading to eventual destruction.

Cells and molecules are not the simplest, most foundational components of nature though. We can look at our physical surroundings on an even simpler level: the level of physical principles. One of these foundational physical principles, one that we each learned in middle school, is the conservation of energy. Energy cannot be created or destroyed, but can only change forms. Conservation is reiterated throughout the sciences, expressed in such forms as the principles of conservation of matter and conservation of mass. In our human lives, we are familiar with the concept of conservation. We know that our garbage doesn't just disappear, but it fills landfills. Dead plants and animals don't just evaporate, but they decay and degrade over time. Dead, broken and malfunctioning things turn into other things when they die. When we consider the cellular waste removal system, the principle of conservation raises a question. Where do cells put the malfunctioning, broken and degenerating components that they target and tag as 'trash?'

Cells are equipped with three systems that all destroy their own components: the **autophagosome**, the **lysosome**, and the **proteasome**. Though the details vary, the basic function is the same: these systems take out the trash. All three protein-destruction systems recognize their targets by identifying molecular tags that have been attached to them. The molecular tags are in fact ubiquitin proteins, functioning in these situations as a kiss of death. Once recognized, the target is chopped up into tiny pieces (Baba 1994; Bainton 1981; Peters 1994).

These tiny pieces are, of course, short segments of amino acids, and the digested protein pieces don't just get dumped into a cellular landfill. They comprise the starting materials that our cells then repurpose and use as building blocks when forming new proteins. The busted, worn out, useless garbage is targeted, chopped up into tiny pieces and rebuilt into new, young proteins and organelles. Nothing in our cells ever goes away completely. It just takes on a new form. The broken pieces are transformed into the precise proteins and organelles that the cell needs in that moment.

Cell component destruction is natural and controlled (Peters 1994). It's regulated, not haphazard. Mechanisms of cell component destruction are multi-step pathways, and they're specific, targeted and regulated in a manner that prevents unwarranted destruction. These destructive mechanisms are part of the cell itself, and are initiated within the cell. In these contexts, destruction does not come from attackers outside of the cell but it is part of life itself. Without it, the continuation of life would not be possible. Destruction is a part of normal cell biology.

If it weren't for the junk, the chopped-up pieces of old, degenerating, broken and malfunctioning proteins, life could not continue. Cells are the original recycling systems, taking their garbage and repurposing it to become something useful and life-giving. In the cellular realm, death is the engine that powers life.

Cells tell a story that is strikingly different from the story of degeneration and meaninglessness that I was trained to find in the "fallen world." Death appears to be a destructive force only when it's observed in isolated incidents and on a small scale. If I step away, disentangling myself and bringing the entire cycle into view, I can see what's really happening. Death is the engine that powers the progress of life. Destruction allows for generation of new things to occur. Death provides the building blocks for the formation of new life. New cells are formed out of the same molecules that originally composed the cells that have become old, busted, broken and dead. Life, death and rebirth, tell one collective story in relationship with one another, and no single phase reveals the totality of that story. It's a pattern that is bigger than any individual step; a continuous, self-perpetuating cycle.

When I laid in that coffin, performing that ritual night after night that evoked imaginations of my own death, it seemed obvious to me that the universe trends toward decay and degeneration. We all are bound by the progress of time and with its persistent forward march, our bodies break down, slow down and succumb to disease. Our capacity for memory dwindles. **Entropy** increases over time. My evangelical community provided a concise narrative that explained all of this. We believed that since we lived in a fallen world, degeneration was natural. I believed that the world was fallen, so I learned to look for its degeneration everywhere. Once I found evidence that fit this narrative of degeneration, I stopped considering any other possible explanations. I stopped short of seeing the full picture. Destruction and death are real, but by no means do they encompass the full story. A much larger story is playing out, but I was blind to anything that didn't reinforce my belief that earth was governed by sin, degeneration, destruction and decay.

It was only when I started to question my belief in the world's sinfulness and degeneration that I was able to start to see through a different lens. I could finally begin to see through the kaleidoscope. Cell behaviors have a particular power to open my eyes, minimizing my emotional entanglements and allowing me to zoom out enough to see a bigger picture. When I zoomed out, I could finally see that generation, degeneration and regeneration are all phases of one single narrative: a looped, continuous cycle that is headed toward new life at every stage.

As an evangelical, I believed that death was my ultimate enemy and eternal life would be the antidote to death. Biology illustrates a completely different relationship between death and life. In biological systems, death and life are part of one single cycle: regeneration. Regeneration is simply rearrangement of fundamental elements. These fundamental elements endure throughout continuous transformations, living eternally in diverse manifestations.

Death is not the enemy of life, but living systems engage in a cycle of life and death. One arrangement of matter exists for a while. Eventually, that arrangement is broken down, stripped away and undone. Then, just when it seems obvious that nothing new or living could ever come out of it again, a brand-new arrangement emerges, reformed, restructured and reordered. The cycle continues over and over again, and each one of these patterns is part of one narrative, a story that transcends but includes all of them at once. Our world is like a kaleidoscope and biological systems are themselves images at the end of the chamber, visible for a time, and then with every turn of the kaleidoscope, they shift, morph and transform into something brand new. It's a constantly changing pattern, and there will always be another pattern yet to be seen.

Whether we're considering molecules, proteins, cells, or human bodies, the central truth remains the same: Eternal life is simply a biological reality. It's the way the natural world works. Degeneration and destruction occur, but they're only temporary phases within a greater cycle. Regeneration always follows destruction.

What happens if I re-examine Jesus' words about eternal life in light of this biological reality? His words become far more than simply a litmus test, but an invitation for his followers to open their eyes to the reality that death is not final. Everything in the natural world is part of a cycle that includes life, death and rebirth. It's a cycle of regeneration. In this light, Jesus' words about eternal life awaken us to the reality that our souls are no different from the eternally persisting natural world. He was clueing us into the reality that we *do* last forever. The story of Jesus' resurrection, in this light, is not just an anomalous miracle, but is an illustration of a central, pervasive and true theme of the universe. You and I are momentary patterns in a constantly changing landscape. There's a human story that started long before we were here and will continue after we're gone. The molecules that compose us will go on to compose other momentary patterns in this forever-changing landscape — new people, living new lives. Our biology clues us into the regenerative power of life.

As an evangelical, I believed I had a purpose that transcended my own life. I believed that God had specifically selected me for salvation and directly handed me the formula for assuring my heavenly destination. I believed that I was chosen and set apart. I now cringe at the distorted self-inflation that stemmed from this belief, but beneath all of the ego-puffing, my belief in eternal life gave me a profound sense of personal purpose. I believed I was on Earth for a reason and that I could fulfill my divine destiny by serving God and evangelizing my neighbors so they'd have eternal life too. When I lost my fundamentalism, I also lost this sense of purpose.

The reality of regeneration changes all of that. Imprinted in my biology, there is a pattern of continuous and dynamic transformation. Each pattern is related to the next, made out of the same elements, but each is a brand-new manifestation. The beauty of each pattern is found in its uniqueness. There are no isolated individuals, but each is a member of an emergent whole whose beauty far exceeds that of any one part. We each occupy a unique place in the human story, but our impermanence need not imply emptiness or meaninglessness. Because of our eternally transforming life, there's meaning and purpose in living well. We will live forever, regenerated continuously and always manifesting anew. We, who contain eternal possibilities, will be recycled and regenerated through infinite iterations as the cosmic kaleidoscope turns.

10

THE FOG

The Prophet's voice still rang in my ears while the acoustic guitarist softly strummed a familiar major-key chord progression. The walk back to my seat felt like it took years. My knees quivered and my adrenaline surged. I had just heard God's personal message, crafted specifically for me and directly delivered to me through the Prophet. In my ears, his message was unprecedented and far from ordinary. I believed his words carried divine power. It was the kind of power I could feel in my body, in the racing of my heart and the trembling of every limb.

There was something about the Prophet's words that surprised me. I thought this would be the night I'd receive some clarity. I thought that after hearing from the Prophet, I'd know for sure what God's plan was for me. Instead, I got a harbinger of disorientation. In my future, there would be a "fog." Confusion, doubt, fear and uncertainty were coming my way.

My legs felt like lead by the time I made it back to my seat. This had to be my fault somehow. Had I sinned too much? Did I simply not deserve the clarity that other people seemed to receive? Why had I been singled out? Yes, the

Prophet gave me the assurance of God's provision throughout the "fog," but I found little comfort in that. How would
I even be able to see clearly enough through the fog to recognize God's provision?

At the time, a fog sounded like a danger that would destroy my faith. My spiritual goal was to see God clearly and
to know him with full certainty. I wanted to know God's
characteristics, desires and traits precisely, and a fog would
obscure my vision, taking away my clarity and certainty.
Spiritual growth, I believed, would lead me closer and
closer to God, so that one day I'd be so in-tune with God
that I'd be able to discern his will in any situation. This
prophecy seemed to remove me even further from that goal.

Certainty and clarity seemed to be such obvious and noble goals. These were essential qualities of every other aspect of my daily life. In order to move through the world, I
needed to have certainty. I needed to use precision. The
happiness and health of my relationships seemed to be built
on clarity of communication. My academic progress was
based on clarity of understanding. Even my daily routines
required clarity of communication and instruction. It was
important to know whether my parents expected me to be
home at 9:00 pm or at 10:00 pm. It was important to know
whether my homeschool history reading assignment was
chapter 10 or chapter 12. There was a correct way to run the
washing machine, a way that was most efficient and effective, and any other way was incorrect. When I learned to
drive, I learned that an absence of clarity and certainty
could be fatal. There was a proper way to interpret road
signs, and misinterpretations could end lives.

Science is no different. In scientific research, certainty
and clarity are highly valued, and failure to measure accurately or communicate precisely can devastate the reliability
of research findings. In fact, when compared with many
other realms, the stakes are even higher within the realm of
science. Hospitals, bridges, apartment buildings, vaccines

and airplanes only exist because of scientific clarity and certainty. Strict rules govern the communication of scientific data, ensuring precision and accuracy. There are correct and incorrect ways of structuring experiments, collecting data and communicating findings. Science itself can be seen as an effort to eradicate mysteries and sharpen definitions.

Within the realm of science, though, this commitment to clarity and certainty leads to a surprising outcome. Scientific investigation illuminates realities that cannot be fully encompassed using the precise, concrete tools that are used to conduct the investigation. Consider gravity, for example. There are aspects of gravity that can be described, measured and quantified with precision and certainty. Gravity impacts every aspect of our physical experience. It surrounds us, and we can precisely measure and predict its effects. We can quantify those effects and communicate them with exactness. We can predict the gravitational force in real or hypothetical situations with a high level of certainty. Gravity is the force that holds the universe together. Without it, the planets would no longer remain in orbit and galaxies would no longer remain bound together. Gravity is necessary for our physiological function. Everything in our universe, from electrons to cardiovascular systems to lunar bodies provides an opportunity for us to understand the force of gravity more fully, and without this fundamental force, all of these functions would be completely disrupted.

In the midst of all of this certainty, logic and precision, though, there's something much grander and stranger going on. Where does the force of gravity originate? It seems as though every object with mass intuitively knows that it should move toward other objects with mass. How can it be that this tendency is inherent in every piece of unthinking, unconscious matter in the universe? How is it that all of matter seems to agree upon this universal law, producing the predictable, measurable and thoroughly reliable phenomenon of gravity? Gravity, the natural reality that we can probe, measure, quantify and confirm is also a grand mystery with unknown origins. Our measurements, quantifications and observations can illuminate the phenomenon, but cannot tell us where it comes from or how it's consistently upheld.

Biology is undergirded by mysteries of its own. Biological data, carefully and precisely collected according to strictly regulated methods, points to mysterious unknown realities. Among these mysteries is the force pushing life forward, the force of survival. Bacterial cells develop sophisticated skills that allow them to dodge the fatal effects of antibiotics, even in the absence of a leader or a teacher. How is it that this pattern of survival—the persistent adaptive preference for continuation of the species—arises in communities of unconscious, unthinking cells? They actively deflect the assaults of attackers, adapting in response to their most recent encounters, continuously obtaining new skills that allow them to survive and thrive. Not only this, but entire populations of bacterial cells follow this pattern in concert with one another, cooperating in such a way that their collective existence is upheld and their community is strengthened. As scientists, we can measure, observe, study and manipulate this enduring pattern of survival. The scientific method, however, can never tell us where this drive toward survival comes from, or how it continues to be upheld. Biology is built out of concise definitions, careful measurements and precise predictions, but the ultimate function of biological investigation is to point to realities that are beyond explanation.

Absurd and mysterious patterns are inextricably woven throughout cell life. Cells build organs and organisms, which are communities that emerge from individual, seemingly discrete entities. In humans, what begins as a single cell grows to become an embryo, which becomes a fetus, then becomes a viable infant, and eventually becomes an adult with distinct, differentially functioning cells. In the initial stages of embryonic development, the new cells are exact replicas of the originals, but out of this sameness emerges the vibrant and diverse tapestry of the human body. Kidney cells, brain cells, skin cells, blood cells, lung cells and pancreatic cells all arise from a single origin. All of these diverse cell types contain an identical DNA molecule, a single source of identity. Diversity, difference and specificity emerge out of simplicity.

As a young evangelical, I believed I could only achieve spiritual growth through certainty. I believed that precise literal biblical interpretation would guide me toward a clear and certain understanding of God. I sought to silence my internal impulses and rely on this guidance in order to ensure my own continuation along the best path.

Cell growth and development proceed according to quite a different model, however. There is no outside guide that directs a cell toward growth and development. A fertilized egg does not contain the entire recipe for developing into a human adult, but it contains profound potential: a DNA molecule and all of the intrinsic machinery necessary for manipulating that genetic code. The cell is not an isolated individual, but is part of an organ, which itself is part of a body. It needs to function in a way that contributes to the health of that body, but from the perspective of one cell, the full biology of the body is a mystery. Cells need guidance. They receive it through their own sensitivity to their environments. This is how cells are able to navigate their lives.

The surfaces of cells are dotted with molecular loading docks which recognize signaling molecules that are sent as messengers from neighboring cells. When a signaling molecule docks on a cell surface receptor, it triggers a sequence of molecular reactions inside the cell. These reactions steer the cell's function. They determine the cell's priorities and dictate the use of its abundant and versatile resources. It's because of its sensitivity to these signaling molecules that a cell is able to participate in its community.

It is only as a result of molecular communication that a cell knows how and when to use its tools. The cell requires signals, specific direction and nuance and it finds these only through interacting with its neighbors. A cell needs to know when and where to express certain regions of its genome. It needs to know how rapidly to proliferate. It needs to know when, where and how to start assigning specific roles to its daughter cells. These decisions to specialize daughter cells are only made through a cell's relationship to the members of its community. Individual cells, incomplete and insufficient on their own, form communities whose capabilities far transcend their individual capacities.

The fact that any of our bodies exist is a testament to the power of community. We are collaborative communities, complete with diversified organs that are organized and connected with one another in an efficient and functional way. We emerged from individuals that lacked the guidance to allow for that development. Our cells learned how to respond to their environmental signals. They learned how to do things like migrate to particular areas of their organs in order to heal wounds left by traumatic incidents or invaders. They learned how to diversify themselves in just the right ratios, so that our brains, lungs, noses and hearts would all become appropriate sizes. They learned the difference between the front, back, top, bottom, left side and right side of our bodies and they oriented themselves accordingly.

As a 14-year-old waiting in the sanctuary aisle, I expected the Prophet to deliver a clear recipe for my life. Instead, what I received was a reminder that no such recipe is available. God's perfect plan would be obscured by a fog. I was told to go slowly in times of transition. I was told to pay attention at the interchanges. I was told to remain sensitive.

At the time, I was terrified of the fog. I thought it would hinder my spiritual growth. Anything that would obscure my view of God was my enemy, I thought. I believed I needed to be certain about who God was and what God wanted me to do, or else I would surely go astray. In retrospect, I see the Prophet's foretelling of the fog as a different type of warning. It was a reminder that the only way my growth would be healthy would be for it to always be guided by my experiences and relationships. The only type of guidance I would have in the midst of the fog would be the imminent guidance provided by my community. I'd have to remain sensitive in order to receive that guidance.

The continuous provision of these imminent signals allows for new creations to emerge. This is the model of development that allows embryos to become adults, seeds to become trees and tadpoles to become frogs. This step-by-step development doesn't require a complete and perfect plan; it only requires guidance for one step at a time.

The fear I felt when I received my prophecy was warranted. My fundamentalist Christian faith, which was the bedrock of my childhood and adolescence crumbled when I encountered the fog. Soon after arriving at my public university, I lost the certainty and clarity required for my fundamentalist views. I had to find a way to move forward through the fog itself, not only through times of certainty and clarity. I was realizing that the fog wasn't clearing anytime soon, but that I was at my best when learning and growing. I was no longer interested in maintaining the static state that allows for certainty and clarity. In order for my understanding of God to be meaningful, I had to find a way that God could stay with me through the fog.

As I came to terms with this, I began to see that I needed

new thought patterns; new ways of framing my beliefs. I began to move beyond systems of binary opposition, into concepts of transcendence and inclusion. Only then could I conceive of a type of God that I could worship even in the midst of uncertainty. I gave up my futile attempts at using logic to prove that faith in God is reasonable. Instead I started searching for beauty and grace, love and unity in my world and seeking to magnify these wherever I found them. I set aside my questions about whether I have free will or am bound by destiny, and begin to embrace the notion that destiny and choice are interwoven, constantly interacting factors that are impossible to disentangle. I stopped my obsessive efforts to rid myself of those pervasive tendencies that I just couldn't seem to avoid, the behaviors I believed were sins. I spent my energy trying to avoid hurting myself and others, instead of obsessively trying to align my thoughts and actions with church-sanctioned standards of holiness. I learned to halt the first step of my self-hatred spiral. I started trying to create heaven on earth for myself and others, rather than fearing that my weaknesses and insufficiencies would send me to hell when I'd die.

When I started to develop this new understanding of God—a God that remained with me in the fog—I became freer. I used to give my energy to self-criticism, self-hatred and desperate attempts to believe 'hard enough' and convince myself that I'd one day be admitted to a heavenly afterlife. Once my view started to change, I could redirect that energy. I could focus on my work and my relationships and celebrate the joys of my life, rather than obsessively and futilely chasing flawlessness. It wasn't only the positive emotions that I was able to feel; I was more open to pain and sadness now too. I could work to improve myself and my world, and I could start to look for the good that already existed, rather than believing stubbornly that my world was fallen, sinful, and beyond hope of redemption. It was only when I started to believe that good exists in the world that I could try to cultivate that good. If not for the fog obscuring my clarity and certainty, I never would have been free to find these greater realities. I never would have looked for a way to transcend the never-resolving conflict of binary opposition, set aside this clash and try to include the nuance of as many seemingly opposing positions as possible.

The fog was a gift, and it directed my attention toward my own finitude. The fog helped me to realize that I saw the world not as it is, but through one specific filter. It was only when I paid attention to these particularities that I could begin to exchange my lens for something different. I'll never see the world truly as it is, and none of us can, but now I recognize my own ability to change my lens. Before I could be transfixed by the beauty of the transforming patterns in the kaleidoscope, I first had to recognize my own ability to change those patterns.

Each new image I see at the end of the kaleidoscope — each new interpretation, understanding, representation or idea — is an opportunity to imagine a truth that is big enough to encompass *that* as well. We live in an expanding universe and we are growing, adapting, evolving creatures. There are forces at play in our world that are bigger and deeper than anything we can see, touch, measure, or quantify. We are inspired by our neighbors in ways that we cannot articulate and we are connected with our communities in ways we cannot explain. These inscrutable realities are the ones we encounter in our daily lives, common but mysterious realities like love, ambition, generosity and progress. There are aspects of our experience that cannot be measured, inclinations we each have that cannot be explained, and individual characteristics whose origins cannot be traced. Whatever truth really is, it must include all of this as well.

Certainty, precision and clarity are helpful in our everyday lives, and they've given us medicines, digital data storage, stable architecture and cybersecurity. But they are not the only ways of understanding our world. There are realities that cannot be encompassed with certainty. The process of appreciating these realities—learning to see through a kaleidoscope—is an ongoing evolution. As a modern American Christian, I've been trained to make decisions and judgments by grouping ideas into opposing, mutually exclusive options and then ranking them. I've been trained to look for precise explanations and I'm drawn to organizational structures that fit a hierarchical paradigm.

I do myself a disservice, however, when I extend these habits to my own beliefs about God. The God I want to worship is the God big enough, powerful enough and multifaceted enough to remain meaningful through a fog. The God built out of certainty will disintegrate with the first doubt. I need a God that is bigger and stronger than that.

As a twenty-something vacillating between agnosticism, atheism and apathy, I held that cassette tape recording of my prophecy in my hand once again. It was 2013 and I hadn't felt the plastic exterior of a cassette tape in over a decade. The once-white cassette was now a dingy shade of brownish yellow, and the spools of ribbon rattled inside the plastic when I picked it up. A strip of masking tape across the top of the cassette had been labelled in my mom's familiar handwriting. It read "Beth Prophecy," and in slightly smaller letters directly below was the Prophet's first and last name. I wanted so badly to throw away that cassette tape. I could think of no logical reason to take this prophecy seriously. The Prophet was just a man with a spiritual reputation who had traveled from Florida to Pittsburgh and monologized as an earnest and believing 14-year-old girl clung to every word he said, taking his forewarnings as God's direct and personal messages.

That cassette tape was connected to so much of the emotional baggage of my adolescence. I imagined what I would feel if I threw it in the garbage, finally parting with that emotional baggage. I'd be able to leave behind that sense of dread, that feeling that God had chosen me for a life of confusion. There was something that stopped me from throwing it away, though; something that kept me still fascinated by his words. I couldn't quite dismiss that prophecy.

As ridiculous as it felt to reach this realization, my prophecy really had been fulfilled. I had encountered a fog; a period of confusion and uncertainty, a point at which I could no longer see clearly. Contrary to my 14-year-old assumption, though, the fog had not been a curse. The fog had always been there, and to begin to recognize it was a blessing. The fog allowed me to realize in an altogether new way that I am a limited, finite creature. To claim that I see clearly would be fraudulent. Recognizing the fog was a first and necessary step toward accepting my own limits.

If it weren't for the fog, I might never have sought imminent guidance, the kind of step-by-step community-derived discernment that transforms an embryo into a fully grown adult. I might never have slowed down and learned to pay attention unless I realized I was in the middle of a fog.

I don't pray very often anymore. It feels disingenuous to pray to a God who, if powerful enough to answer my prayers, would be a villain for continuing to allow pain, injustice and trauma to persist in my world. But this God, the one who is omnipotent, omniscient, and in control of everything, is by no means the only type of God I can imagine. Any succinct description of God becomes a way of confining God. While the boundaries drawn around a tightly defined God can give comfort and provide the illusion of certainty, they cannot encompass the profound mysteries of my lived human experience. This is why I'm not interested in worshipping a God that can be succinctly described.

I do have a type of spiritual practice, though. My spiritual practice is my own sensitivity to my experience and relationships. It's my participation in my own community, in something that's greater than me and greater than any individual, but that emerges out of our relationship to one another. Those moments involve genuine connection with others. They involve relationship. They involve celebration of the life force of which I am a part, the same force that directs my cells' development, always observable but never quite comprehensible. This spiritual practice evokes the courage of vulnerability and the patience of empathy. It evokes compassion, sensitivity, and a desire to continue seeing the world from new perspectives. My spiritual practice is seeing my world through the kaleidoscope.

11

EPILOGUE

Through nearly squeezed-shut eyelids I could see just enough to make out the word "Sending..." as it hung near the toolbar of my web browser. All I had to do was wait until that one word changed. I imagined the message racing along the virtual highways of the internet, still in transit now, not yet safely at its destination, but already gone and irretrievably embarking upon its journey. Everything would be easier once the email arrived. Then there would be no taking it back.

I exhaled sharply as soon as the toolbar changed to read "Message Sent." I hadn't even realized I was holding my breath. Even after that heavy sigh, and now breathing normally, I felt nothing even close to the sense of relief I had expected to feel. I'd been so focused on building up the courage to click that ominous "Send" button that I hadn't really thought about what would happen after I clicked it. I thought the sending of that message, an act of raw vulnerability would be the hard part but no—this was the hardest part. Before clicking "Send", I had the manuscript to occupy me. I could continue tinkering with the pages and paragraphs in near perpetuity, treating the act of editing like it was a lightning rod that could absorb all of my anxious energy. I couldn't tinker anymore, at least not with the version my parents would see. All I could do now was wait.

By clicking "Send," I initiated a final step in the first phase of my book manuscript preparation. I sent it to my parents and asked them to read it. Writing a book full of personal stories is dangerous, because no story is solely personal. Everything we experience involves other people, whether they are present with us in those experiences or only present in our minds during those experiences. My childhood stories involve my parents in a direct and overt manner and it was important to me that they sign off on my recounting of their roles in these stories. In the now-sent email, I explained that I would gladly cut out anything they thought misrepresented them, or anything they wouldn't want to be made public. At no point in developing this book did I intend it to be an exposé, a tell-all or a shocking story of childhood spiritual trauma. In fact, I had a good childhood. I was privileged to be so well cared for throughout my young life. I did, however, choose to focus this manuscript on the unhealthy, painful and damaging effects of the sense of shame that was cultivated by my religious upbringing.

My parents requested a few simple changes to the manuscript, which I happily made before sharing it with anyone else. To my surprise, though, it wasn't exactly the content of the book that seemed to catch their attention the most. It was what the book symbolized that really caught their attention. This was the first real glimpse they had of the internal struggle that had enveloped me in shame through my childhood and adolescence, and now led me to completely rethink my beliefs and worldviews. They both wanted to talk to me, they explained, to sit down with me and get a clearer picture of this book's inspiration. We set dates to meet one-on-one.

I sat across the table from my dad, gripping my paper

coffee cup as though it were a wild animal. I ran my right-hand thumbnail underneath the seam of the cardboard coffee cup sleeve, pulling at the glue that held it together. It was sealed too tightly for me to pull it apart, and I couldn't even succeed in getting it to bend. I was barely conscious of that simple frustration, but my anxious energy found a place to land within it, which was suspended in the air around me just a second ago. All of that idle energy found its manifestation in my frustration with the seam of that cardboard coffee cup sleeve. It absorbed the tension and anxiety that I felt about the conversation we were about to have.

I'd woken up early that morning, earlier than I usually do on a Saturday. I woke up with a racing mind, and it was hard to focus on anything beyond rifling through my mental filing cabinet of childhood memories. I consumed my loose, unproductive and frantic energy by heading out for a morning jog.

Before my jog though, I had to write. There were too many thoughts in my head and I needed to give them some organization before I did anything else. I took out the current volume of my Notebook. It was one of my most precious possessions. I kept this Notebook with me at all times, and it was a collection of my deepest thoughts. Sometimes my Notebook served as a journal, sometimes it served as a drawing board for ideas that would later turn into written pieces, and today it served as a conversation guide.

"Ways That Evangelicalism Hurt Me"

Bullet points came to mind easily and the page filled quickly. I knew that I couldn't speak in general terms, or I'd be setting myself up to be dismissed. I knew I couldn't construct anything even close to a "straw man" argument, or I'd be asking for my conclusions to be discounted. The things I was trying to communicate were specific and personal, and the only way to communicate them effectively would be with specific and personal details and examples.

Between fundamentalism and now, what had changed were the relationships I built and the experiences I had. I wanted to tell that story.

Experiential learning was never presented as an esteemed source of knowledge in my church. We relied on doctrines, developed from literally interpreted biblical passages. These doctrines had once given me a sense of safety, constancy and certainty, but now, they created nothing but dissonance. My relationships and my experience had taken me further and further away from these doctrines. I'd developed relationships with plenty of people who did not confess to believe in Jesus, but who still lived genuinely generous, creative and wholehearted lives. Some seemed to give no thought whatsoever to religion, God or spirituality. Some were atheist, some were agnostic, some were Jewish, some were Hindu, some were Muslim and some were Buddhists. The exclusivity of Christianity no longer made any sense to me.

Even my relationships within Christian communities were beginning to challenge the doctrines I grew up believing. I met queer Christians, gay Christians, lesbian Christians and transgender Christians. I met Christians who interpreted Biblical texts as poetic and symbolic documents, rather than inerrant manuscripts that should be read literally. I met Christians who thought that it was important to recognize that the Biblical texts had been heavily influenced by the historical circumstances from which they arose, rather than blindly cutting and pasting these words into modern contexts. Through these relationships, I found peace with many of the things that were forbidden or excluded by the doctrines of my childhood. I could no longer remain at peace with those doctrines.

I wasn't accustomed to drawing on experiential and relational knowledge, at least not in conversations about my faith. My own personal experience, I'd been taught, was not to be trusted. It was uncertain and unsteady ground, as were all foundations other than Christ himself. I was used to discussing my faith solely using fundamental claims, abstract concepts and simple logic to prescribe modern behaviors on the basis of ancient wisdom. This morning would be different. I'd be taking an approach I'd never taken before, venturing into uncharted territory. Still, I had an idea of how best to go about it. I knew that I should make my stories as personal as possible. Debate would potentially drive us further apart, but empathy could bring us closer together.

I began listing bullet points on that page in my Notebook, detailing the roots and outcomes of the shame I felt in our church. I wrote about the doctrine of total human depravity and my own shame and self-hatred that I directly traced to this belief. I wrote about my darkest days, when this self-hatred had convinced me that suicide would be my most prudent path. I wrote about how it was only a few years prior that I'd felt this way, even though I'd never expressed that to anyone but my husband at the time. I wrote about the helplessness I felt when I used to believe that I was responsible for the murder of Jesus of Nazareth even though that killing occurred 2,000 years before I was born. I added specific details, like how I was taught that it wasn't my actions that caused the death of Jesus, but instead my identity as a totally depraved sinner caused his death.

I wrote about the way that our obsession with a heavenly afterlife led me to disengage from life on earth, making my daily life seem like it was either a pointless exercise or a cruel joke, depending on the details of my current circumstances.

I wrote about exclusion of women from leadership roles in our church. I wrote about the subordination of women, perpetuated in our church's teachings about marriage, specifically the teaching that wives should "submit" to their husbands and "obey" their husbands as they would obey the Lord. I wrote about how I felt, when I was taught as a little girl that God, who was exclusively referred to as a "he," created the first female only after creating a male and realizing that he needed a helper.

I wrote about the way that my disbelief, doubt and questions were scolded in our church, and how I was reprimanded or shamed by youth group leaders, accountability partners and small group leaders when I even hinted at questioning our pastors' teachings. I wrote about how I'd had questions for a long time about how the Bible was composed and translated, but when I asked how it came to exist in its modern form, I was given firm answers that weren't really explanatory, and sometimes seemed aggressive. "The Bible is directly from God," I was told, or "the Bible is completely divinely inspired." None of the answers satisfied me, but I could tell that further questions would not be entertained. Our church created a culture where questions were pushed aside, and doubts were seen as dangerous traps rather than opportunities to learn and grow.

I wrote about the dating rules. I wrote about the shame, self-hatred and disillusionment I felt throughout my entire adolescence, when I was taught that human sexuality was dangerous and sinful, that my body was a pitfall, a stumbling block, a distraction and an object of lust. I wrote about how I felt out of place when I started to realize that I didn't want a future as the classic biblical woman esteemed in our church community: a mother and quiet, submissive wife.

While I was growing up, I took all of these doctrines seriously, but I rarely expressed my internal thoughts. I never told my parents about my shame and self-hatred. I have a tendency to keep my thoughts internal, collecting, synthesizing and developing my ideas but usually hesitant to articulate them. As I continued to fill the pages of my Notebook, imagining the conversation I was about to have with my dad, I struggled to think of the actual words I'd use to describe even the beliefs themselves, let alone my rejection of those beliefs. As a child, I had been like a sponge, soaking up every statement, comment, prayer and sermon I heard, taking it all seriously and literally, as I'd been taught. Now, in this conversation with my dad, I was about to wring out that sponge for the very first time.

My right-hand thumbnail still ran up and down the seam of the cardboard coffee cup sleeve, as I sat across the table from my dad. I was anxious for our small talk preamble to conclude. This was my dad, the same person who I'd envisioned as superhuman when I was a child. He was the one who had parented me, had established rules for me to follow and had organized, arranged, planned, financed and counseled me from my birth through the age of 18. In my own eyes, my rejection of the beliefs he himself had delivered to me was a monumental life event. In many ways, my brain and my heart had never grown beyond the seven-year-old I once was, who wanted nothing other than to make him happy.

He was the first to bring up the reason for our meeting.

"I wanted you to know, first and foremost, that I'm sorry. I apologize for how our church hurt you. I never realized how deeply you were internalizing what you were hearing."

When I heard his apology, my Notebook pages, filled with bulleted lists of reasons, details and descriptions suddenly seemed ridiculous. I didn't have to explain anything. He already understood. My anxiety started to dissipate, no match for my dad's understanding, empathy and love. I thought I'd prepared for every possible scenario. I thought that I'd considered every reaction he could possibly have. This was the one reaction I hadn't prepared for, though. It never occurred to me that maybe he, the one who had taught me many of the doctrines I believed when I was young, left room in his belief system for transformation.

We talked about how the world had changed since he first heard the Christian message. He first heard the Christian gospel in the early 1970s, when he was in high school.

We talked about the ways in which his cultural context was drastically different from mine, as a thirty-year-old in 2018. We talked about the increased amount and depth of connection between modern communities across the globe, and how when he was a kid, he didn't really know anyone who wasn't a Christian. My experience in the world has been profoundly different from my dad's when he was my age. We both agreed that in my world, to claim Christianity as the only way of approaching God doesn't make sense. I was taught that to reject Christ would lead to destruction and self-obsession, but I now knew plenty of people who embrace a wide array of religious views, or who rejected religion entirely and were also incredibly kind, generous and loving. I simply could no longer accept a version of the gospel that excludes everyone who doesn't confess belief in Jesus from salvation.

Sitting at that table that morning, my dad and I both admitted and agreed that beliefs, doctrines and ideas about truth can and should expand and transform over time. When I went into the conversation, I was convinced that the Christian framework was far too rigid, exclusive and static to allow for this kind of transformation, but my dad, in just a few sentences, helped me to reconsider. What if I leave behind the restrictive and exclusive elements of the gospel story I was told, but still embrace the hopeful, inclusive elements, the ones that I find to be true in my own lived experience?

We talked about the doctrines that no longer fit with what I know about the world, such as the doctrine of individual redemption. I shared with him about the shame that I felt throughout my adolescence, stemming from my own belief that I was personally responsible for maintaining my own salvation, and helping as many people as possible access their own redemption. He listened patiently and responded thoughtfully, suggesting ways to expand that belief, bringing into consideration the implications of redemption for communities, people groups, and humanity as a whole. Something expansive, transformative and, I believe, divine happened at that table that morning. We together affirmed the pursuit of an evolving, transforming and growing faith.

Our conversation slowly shifted and we moved from discussing theological themes to recounting shared memories. I laughed harder at my childhood self than I had in years, remembering my own quirks and habits with a new fondness. We both cried as we thought about the heartfelt love that we had always had for each other. Once I started to open up space within my beliefs to allow for evolution, transformation and growth, I was able to remember the love that had always formed the foundation of that faith. I could finally give myself permission to hang on to the elements of my faith which filled me with life and joy, while releasing the elements that no longer fit with my own lived experience.

Sitting at that table, for the first time in a long time, I could remember the earnestness with which I embraced my church's doctrines, assertions and statements of faith. I could remember the deep, consistent love that was at the root of my parents' teaching of those doctrines. Once I gave myself permission to expand, transform and grow, I regained the capacity to be grateful for the good that was at the root of my beliefs.

Not all stories of faith transformations end this way. Not all Christian parents are as accepting, inclusive and kind as mine, and all too commonly, expansions and transformations of faith end in severed ties and hurt feelings. My story does not negate the importance and significance of these stories of pain, abandonment and rejection. My story, however, is a reminder that people can change. I'm grateful that I gave my parents the chance to surprise me.

Forgiveness requires the interest, commitment and dedication of all parties, and none of us can control how someone else will react to the transformations of our own beliefs. We can, however, take the first step. And we can actively engage others even when we think we might already know their response. We can choose not to sever ties unless the relationship becomes damaging. We can listen. We can ask thoughtful questions, and we can empathize.

This intentional empathy is essential to any beliefs that I now hold. I'm not sure if I still believe in God, but the only God I'm interested in thinking about is a God that is love. I believe in a love that unifies, not by creating uniformity, but by creating the kind of wild diversity we see as we look through a kaleidoscope. It's the type of diversity we see in the manifestation of metastable epialleles. This is the way I see divergent religious beliefs and differing worldviews. I see them not as competing claims of ultimate truth, but as diverse manifestations of underlying truths. When I encounter new beliefs and ideas, I look for the common ground, the perennial wisdom underlying the specificity of expression. I believe that if there is anything real that can be called the divine, then it certainly must be present in all of us, and that our task is to uncover it, not to beg for it to be delivered to us from an outside source. My hope is not to destroy my deepest desires, but to uncover my truly deepest desires, the ones that are beneath my superficial fleeting desires. I believe there is good in nature and good in humanity, and while that good can certainly be lost or hindered, it can also be embraced, magnified and pursued.

The God that is love is glorified when we magnify the good that is in the world. Compassion, forgiveness, generosity, creativity, conviction and passion will glorify the God that is love. This love is the same love that was always there at the foundation of my Bible memory verses, my youth group teachings and even my church's evangelistic haunted house. That pure love was diluted and polluted with messages of exclusivity, individuality and fear, but I believe we can uncover the foundation of love. I can take the love I find in those memories and cherish it, while setting aside the shame and self-hatred that I also feel in those memories. Now, I pursue a love that does not seek to exclude. I'm in search of the love that does not claim to be the one and only way, but which seeks to find the common ground among many diverse paths.

I find powerful metaphors in the story of Jesus. I find wisdom in this particular set of beliefs, and it's the religious model that's most familiar to me, by far. The Jesus story will always be significant to me. The literal meaning of this story, however, I do not claim to be the only truth. I'm looking for truth that is far bigger, deeper and wider than that. I hope and believe that the deep truth of the universe could never be contained in just one set of metaphors.

Now, my pursuit of the sacred is similar to my pursuit of science. Neither quest is ever complete, yet both are infinitely pursuable. The answers are never final, but they are thoughtfully refined over time. Investigation of the natural world always pushes at the border of certainty, as we continuously seek to understand that which cannot be fully defined. My pursuit of God progresses in exactly the same way. Through turning the kaleidoscope, the transformations are limitless and always novel, each new image enrapturing me with its entirely new beauty. I look through this kaleidoscope and my awe and wonder are always renewed as I see beauty that is richer than I ever before imagined.

References

CHAPTER 2

Ciechanover, A., Heller, H., Elias, S., Hass, A. L. & Hershko, A. (1980). ATP-dependent conjugation of reticulocyte proteins with the polypeptide required for protein degradation. *Proc Natl Acad Sci USA, 77*(3), 1365-8.

Hershko, A., Ciechanover, A., Heller, H., Haas, A. L. & Rose, I. A. (1980). Proposed role of ATP in protein breakdown: conjugation of protein with multiple chains of the polypeptide of ATP-dependent proteolysis. *Proc Natl Acad Sci USA, 77*(4), 1783-6.

Dwane, L., Gallagher, W. M., Chonghaile, T. N. & O'Connor, D. P. (2017). The emerging role of non-traditional ubiquitination in oncogenic pathways. *J Biol Chem, 292*(9), 3543-3551.

Schwertman, P., Bekker-Jensen, S. & Mailand, N. (2016). Regulation of DNA double-strand break repair by ubiquitin and ubiquitin-like modifiers. *Nat Rev, 17*, 379-394.

CHAPTER 3

Duhl, D. M. J., Vrieling, H., Miller, K. A., Wolff, G. L. & Barsh, G. S. (1994). Neomorphic agouti mutations in obese yellow mice. *Nat Genet, 8*(1), 59-65.

Dolinoy, D. (2008). The agouti mouse model: an epigenetic biosensor for nutritional and environmental alterations on the fetal epigenome. *Nutr Rev, 66*, S7-11.

CHAPTER 4

Daignan-Fornier, B. & Sagot, I. (2011). Proliferation/quiescence: the controversial "aller-retour". *Cell Div,* 6(1), 10.

Schneider, C., King, R. M. & Philipson, L. (1988). Genes specifically expressed at growth arrest of mammalian cells. *Cell,* 54(6), 787-793.

Coppock, D. L., Kopman, C., Scandalis, S. & Gilleran, S. (1993). Preferential gene expression in quiescent human lung fibroblasts. *Cell Growth Differ,* 4(6), 483-493.

Coller, H. A., Sang, L. & Roberts, J. M. (2006). A New Description of Cellular Quiescence. *PLoS Biol,* 4(3), e83.

CHAPTER 5

Ochman, H., Lawrence, J. G. & Groisman, E. A. (2000). Lateral gene transfer and the nature of bacterial innovation. *Nature,* 405(6784), 299-304.

Keeling, P. J.; Palmer, J. D. (2008). Horizontal gene transfer in eukaryotic evolution. *Nat Rev Gen,* 9, 605-18.

Dunning Hotopp, J. C. (2011). Horizontal gene transfer between bacteria and animals. *Trends Genet,* 27(4), 157-163.

Lacroix, B. & Citovsky, V. (2016). Transfer of DNA from Bacteria to Eukaryotes. *MBio,* 7(4), e00863-00816.

CHAPTER 6

Koshland, D. E. (2002). The Seven Pillars of Life. *Science,* 295(5563), 2215-2216.

CHAPTER 7

Lodish, H., Berk, A., Matsudaira, P., Kaiser, C. A., Krieger, M., Scott, M. P., Zipursky, S. L. & Darnell, J. (2004). *Molecular Biology of the Cell* (5th ed.). New York, NY: WH Freeman.

Lehmann, A. R., Nimi, A., Ogi, T., Brown, S., Sabbioneda, S., Wing, J. F., Kannouche, P. L. &

Green, C. M. (2007). Translesion synthesis: Y-family polymerases and the polymerase switch. *DNA Repair, 6*(7), 891-8.

CHAPTER 8
Ainsworth, C. (2015). Sex Redefined. *Nature, 518*(7539), 288-291.

Berta, P., Hawkins, J. B., Sinclair, A.H., Taylor, A., Griffiths, B. L., Goodfellow, P. N. & Fellous, M. (1990). Genetic evidence equating SRY and the testis-determining factor. *Nature, 348*(6300), 448-450.

CHAPTER 9
Baba, M., Takeshige, K., Baba, N. & Ohsumi, Y. (1994). Ultrastructural analysis of the autophagic process in yeast: detection of autophagosomes and their characterization. *J Cell Biol, 124*(6), 903-13.

Bainton, D. F. (1981). The discovery of lysosomes. *J Cell Biol, 91*(3 Pt 2), 66s-76s.

Peters, J. M. (1994). Proteasomes: protein degradation machines of the cell. *Trends Biochem Sci, 19*(9), 377-82.

GLOSSARY

Cell: 1. An autonomous self-replicating unit that may exist as functional independent unit of life (as in the case of unicellular organism), or as sub-unit in a multicellular organism (such as in plants and animals) that is specialized into carrying out particular functions towards the cause of the organism as a whole. 2. A membrane-bound structure containing biomolecules, such as nucleic acids, proteins, and polysaccharides.

Organelle: A membrane-bound compartment or structure in a cell that performs a special function.

Protein: A molecule composed of polymers of amino acids joined together by peptide bonds. It can be distinguished from fats and carbohydrates by containing nitrogen. Other components include carbon, hydrogen, oxygen, sulfur, and sometimes phosphorus

DNA: A double-stranded nucleic acid that contains the genetic information for cell growth, division, and function.

Gene: The fundamental, physical, and functional unit of heredity. Genes are defined segments of DNA molecules.

Cell Biology: the branch of biology dealing with the study of cells, especially their formation, structure, components, and function. (1)

Molecular Biology: the branch of biology that deals with the nature of biological phenomena at the molecular level through the study of DNA and RNA, proteins, and other macromolecules involved in genetic information and cell function, characteristically making use of advanced tools and techniques of separation, manipulation, imaging, and analysis. (2)

DNA replication: The process of copying and duplicating a DNA molecule in a semiconservative way, i.e. the copy contains one of the original strands paired with a newly synthesized strand that is complementary in terms of AT and GC base pairing

Mitosis: The process where a single cell divides resulting in generally two identical cells, each containing the same number of chromosomes and genetic content as that of the original cell.

Gene expression: The conversion of the information from the gene into mRNA via transcription and then to protein via translation resulting in the phenotypic manifestation of the gene.

Transcription: It is the process of transcribing or making a copy of genetic information stored in a DNA strand into a complementary strand of RNA (messenger RNA or mRNA) with the aid of RNA polymerases.

Translation: A step in protein biosynthesis where a genetic code from a strand of mRNA is decoded to produce a particular sequence of amino acids.

Enzyme: A catalyst or a chemical produced by cells to generally speed up specific chemical reaction without changing the chemical reaction at the end of the reaction

DNA Lesion: Any pathological or traumatic discontinuity of DNA, often leading to loss of function of one or multiple genes.

Cell Cycle: The sequence of growth and division of a cell, and consists of a series of biological processes, particularly the resting phase (G0), the interphase (G1, S, G2), and cell division (i.e. mitosis and cytokinesis).

Polymerase enzymes: A group of enzymes that catalyze the synthesis of nucleic acids on preexisting nucleic acid templates, assembling RNA from ribonucleotides or

DNA from deoxyribonucleotides. An enzyme that catalyzes the formation of new DNA and RNA from an existing strand of DNA or RNA

Proliferation: The reproduction or multiplication of similar forms, especially of cells and morbid cysts.

Allele: One member of a pair (or any of the series) of genes occupying a specific spot on a chromosome (called locus) that controls the same trait.

Embryogenesis: The processes leading to the development of an embryo from egg to completion of the embryonic stage.

Chromosome: A structure within the cell that bears the genetic material as a threadlike linear strand of DNA bonded to various proteins in the nucleus of eukaryotic cells, or as a circular strand of DNA (or RNA in some viruses) in the cytoplasm of prokaryotes and in the mitochondrion and chloroplast of certain eukaryotes.

Autophagosome: The vesicle (or organelle) that conducts a programmed cell death characterized by biochemical events leading to self-digestion through the destructive action of enzymes produced by the cell itself, often as a defensive or self-preservation response

Lysosome: Organelle containing a large range of digestive enzymes used primarily for digestion and removal of excess or worn-out organelles, food particles, and engulfed viruses or bacteria.

Proteasome: proteolytic complexes that degrade cytosolic and nuclear proteins.

Entropy: The amount of disorder in a system.

Unless otherwise specified, all definitions are found in *Biology-Online Dictionary*. Retrieved August 19, 2017 from Biology-Online website http://www.biology-online.org

cell biology. (n.d.). *Dictionary.com Unabridged*. Retrieved August 19, 2017 from Dictionary.com website http://www.dictionary.com/browse/cell-biology

molecular biology. (n.d.). *Dictionary.com Unabridged.* Retrieved August 19, 2017 from Dictionary.com website http://www.dictionary.com/browse/cell-biology

ABOUT THE AUTHOR

When she was a very young girl, Elizabeth Jeffries decided she would one day become a scientist. Nothing sounded more exciting than exploring the unknown. By the time she reached college, Elizabeth chose to pursue a career in the biomedical sciences, and after completing a BS in chemistry at Indiana University of Pennsylvania, received a PhD in chemistry from the University of Pittsburgh. Her dissertation research introduced her to the universe of biological molecules, and the powerful biochemical tools that can unravel processes and pathways within human cells. Elizabeth continued went on to receive a postdoctoral appointment at the University of Pittsburgh Medical Center, where she investigated the cellular mechanisms of aging in a laboratory research setting.

Elizabeth's love for the natural sciences took on new meaning when the evangelical fundamentalist Christian faith of her childhood began to disintegrate. This transformation of her faith landed Elizabeth in a place of newfound instability, and the concrete natural world provided her with a sense of meaning and wonder in the midst of it. In the absence of theological certainty, writing about nature became Elizabeth's way of affirming life. Today, Elizabeth writes in a variety of scientific and medical contexts, in both professional and creative capacities.

ABOUT THE PUBLISHER

Epiphany Publishing, LLC is a private publishing company based in Indianapolis, Indiana. We are devoted to exploring catalysts for growth in the fields of religion, psychology, business, and human development.

Each year, Epiphany Publishing donates at least 25% of all its profits to nonprofit organizations that fight profound injustice — especially those atrocities that rob the innocent of their future. This includes the global sex trade, child soldiers forced to fight in war, and other forms of unthinkable oppression. We invite you to join us in partnering with luminous, restorative organizations making a difference in the world like saribari.com, warchild.org, worldvision.org, and antislavery.org.

We are always interested in meeting new authors and reviewing promising manuscripts. If you've got a transformational message that you believe would be a good fit to publish with us, please introduce yourself at epiphany-publishing.us.

47329033R00135

Made in the USA
Middletown, DE
11 June 2019